Contents

Acknowledgements
The publishers wish to thank the following for permission to use copyright material: Greenpeace UK for the leaflet *How Far Should We Go to Protect the Planet?*; HarperCollins Publishers for the excerpt from *The Flying Machine* by Ray Bradbury; SCAA/DFEE for excerpts from the Key Stage 3 Teachers' Booklets.

First published in 1997 by
Stanley Thornes (Publishers) Ltd
Ellenborough House
Wellington Street
CHELTENHAM
GL50 1YW

97 98 99 00 \ 10 9 8 7 6 5 4 3 2 1

A catalogue record for this book is available from the British Library

ISBN 0 7487 3131 8

Designed and typeset by Ian Foulis & Associates, Saltash ,Cornwall
Illustrated by Mike Miller and Ian Foulis & Associates

Printed and bound in Great Britain by The Baskerville Press, Salisbury, Wiltshire

Introduction

What this book contains

During your child's third year in secondary school (Year 9) he or she will sit Key Stage 3 National Assessment Tests in the three core subjects: English, mathematics and science. These tests take place in school over a period of about a week during May and the results are reported back to you. For each of the three subjects your child will be given a mark in the form of a level. Most children will perform in the range of Levels 4–6 by the end of Key Stage 3, with an average performance being roughly Level 5.

The tests are a valuable measure of your child's performance over the first three years of secondary school and give an indication of their likely performance at Key Stage 4, which leads to the GCSE examinations.

This book provides you with one complete set of practice papers for each of the three subjects with the principle aim of preparing your child confidently for the tests. Each set of papers will:

- provide test questions similar to those in the National Tests for Key Stage 3 of the National Curriculum;
- give your child practice in sitting the tests: working to a set time, getting familiar with the format and style of the tests and developing effective test strategies;
- give a broad guide to your child's likely level of performance within Levels 3–8 of each subject (Levels 4–7 in maths);
- give you an idea of strengths and weaknesses in your child's learning.

Helping your child sit tests

As well as practising the content of the tests, one of the key aims of this book is to give your child practice in working under test conditions. All the tests are timed and your child should try to complete each one within the given time. In order to make best use of the tests, and to ensure that the experience is a positive one for your child, it is helpful to follow a few basic principles:

- Talk with your child first before embarking on the tests. Present the activity positively and reassuringly. Encourage your child to view doing the papers as an activity which will help, always making him or her feel secure about the process.
- Ensure that your child is relaxed and rested before doing a test. It may be better to do a paper at the weekend or during the holidays rather than straight after a day at school.
- Ensure a quiet place, free from noise or disturbance, for doing the tests.
- Ensure that there is a watch or clock available.
- Ensure that your child understands exactly what to do for each paper and give some basic test strategies for tackling the task. For example:
  - Try to tackle all the questions but don't worry if you can't do some. Put a pencil mark by any you can't do, leave them and come back at the end.
  - Make sure you read the questions carefully.
  - Go straight on to the next page when each is finished.

- Try to pace yourself over the allowed time. Look over the whole paper first to get an idea of how many questions there are and how much each one covers. Don't spend too long over one question or part of a question.

- Use all your time.

- If you have any time over at the end go back over your answers. This is particularly important if you are doing one big piece of work, such as writing an essay.

- Taking the time to talk over a test beforehand and to discuss any difficulties afterwards will really help your child to gain confidence in the business of sitting tests.

- However your child does, ensure that you give plenty of praise for effort.

What to do with the results

The tests in this book and the results gained from them are only a guide to your child's likely level of performance. They are not an absolute guarantee of how your child will actually perform in the National Tests themselves. However, these papers will at least allow your child to get practice in sitting tests; they will also give *you* an insight into the strengths and weaknesses in their learning.

If there are particular areas of performance which seem weaker, it may be worth providing more practice of the skills required. It is also valuable to discuss any such weaknesses with your child's subject teacher, and to seek confirmation of any problem areas and advice on how to proceed. It is always better to work in partnership with the school if you can. Above all ensure that you discuss these issues with your child in a positive and supportive way so that you have their co-operation in working together to improve learning.

ENGLISH

Testing your child's English

What do the National Tests cover?

Almost all secondary pupils aged 11 to 14 are taught the National Curriculum for English. Towards the end of Year 9, they are tested on what they know, understand and can do in *two* of its three Sections (called Attainment Targets):

- Attainment Target 2: Reading
- Attainment Target 3: Writing

Pupils are **not** formally tested in **Attainment Target 1**, Speaking and Listening. This is continuously assessed in school by their English teachers.

What do these practice papers cover?

There are **two** test papers. They combine the assessment of Reading and Writing in roughly equal proportions. Each paper, however, tests different aspects of your child's reading and writing skills.

Paper 1 (time: 1½ hours + 15 minutes reading time)

- **Section A:** a reading test based on an extract from a story or some other form of descriptive writing.
- **Section B:** a second reading test based on a piece of informative writing (e.g. a non-fiction leaflet, pamphlet or advertisement).
- **Section C:** an extended writing test in which your child can choose to write a story (real or imagined), an article for a newspaper/magazine, or a piece of argument.

Paper 1 is illustrated in full on pages 7 to 19.

Paper 2 (time 1¼ hours)

This paper tests your child's knowledge and understanding of the Shakespeare play s/he has studied at school during Year 9 – *Julius Caesar*, **or** *A Midsummer Night's Dream* **or** *Romeo and Juliet*.

Two tasks are set on different scenes from the chosen play. Your child must do one of these, with the help of a booklet in which the scene on which s/he decides to answer is printed.

Paper 2 is illustrated in full on pages 23 to 40.

How are the test marks arrived at?

Answers on both papers are assessed according to a mark scheme laid down by the body responsible for National Curriculum standards (SCAA). This ensures that the work of pupils in all schools is measured against the same yardstick.

The mark scheme is applied to Papers 1 and 2 in the following way:

- **Paper 1, Section A.** This is marked purely for your child's *understanding* of the reading passage set. The way in which his/her answers are written is not assessed.
- **Paper 1, Section B.** This is marked for your child's ability to describe how the text in question *influences the reader*. Again, no marks are given or subtracted for the way in which the answer is written.
- **Paper 1, Section C.** This is marked partly for the content and partly for the style of your child's writing. The most important factors are: *originality* of ideas, the overall *structure* of the writing, and the *quality of expression* shown (including vocabulary, spelling, grammar and punctuation).

The mark scheme for Paper 1 is illustrated on pages 11–13, 17 and 19.

- **Paper 2, Shakespeare**. This paper is marked for (a) Understanding and Response and (b) Written Expression. The former tests your child's *understanding* of Shakespeare's language and his/her personal *response* to the play's story, characters and themes. The latter tests your child's ability to *construct* a clear, well-detailed answer and to write in a style *suitable to the ideas expressed*.

Mark schemes for Paper 2 are illustrated on pages 27, 33 and 39.

How are test marks linked to a National Curriculum Level?

There are ten levels of attainment in the National Curriculum, covering the age-range five to sixteen. By the end of Key Stage 3, most pupils are expected to achieve a level between 4 and 7. Level 5 is the most common.

Your child will be awarded a final score for the *whole* English test. This equates with National Curriculum Levels 4 to 7 inclusive. An 'exceptional performance' can earn above Level 7. A small number of pupils with serious learning difficulties may not reach Level 4.

'How to find an overall Level for your child' is described on page 41.

Does attainment in school contribute to the test mark?

No. Results of the test, which is a *national* one, are published separately from those for school coursework in English. Included in the latter are attainments for oral work and other parts of the English syllabus which a one-off test cannot assess.

Why does the test matter?

The test will show how your child's skills in English measure up to the standards set out in the National Curriculum. The results will give you a yardstick by which to compare his/her attainments with others in the school and in the country as a whole. Many schools use test results at age 14 to place pupils in an appropriate GCSE teaching group for English. This could have a bearing on GCSE grades.

Using this section of the book

- Working slavishly through a set of practice papers is a useful but relatively limited exercise for Key Stage 3 pupils. Therefore the material that follows is designed as a teaching and learning resource. It provides advice and instruction for pupils as they attempt each part of the test. The questions and tasks used are as near to the 'real thing' as it is possible to make them.

- After each part of the test, a demonstration is given of how to assess your child's level of achievement. Page 41 provides a simple method of calculating an overall English test grade.

- As a parent, *your* involvement in your child's work on the practice papers is of great importance. It will instil confidence and considerably assist your child's progress if you:

  - discuss with your child his/her reactions to each part of the test immediately after doing it;

  - mark your child's work together with him/her, sharing the relevant mark scheme as you do so;

  - attempt, if possible, the whole of Paper 1 yourself at the same time as your child;

  - ensure that your child sees a good quality stage-production (not just a video) of the Shakespeare play s/he is doing for the test.

- Success in any formal test or examination results from a 'triangular' relationship between pupil, school and parent. One intention of this part of the book is to increase your own knowledge of what the Key Stage 3 English Test actually involves and how it is assessed. A book such as this, of course, can only address itself to a general readership. Therefore, if you have any queries or concerns about the specific work your child is doing in preparation for the test, you should contact his/her school's English department.

Read the following passage. Then answer question 1 and question 2.

The passage comes from an imaginary story, set in ancient China. It is about the first person ever to invent a flying machine.

In the year AD 400, the Emperor Yuan held his throne by the Great Wall of China, and the land was green with rain, readying itself towards the harvest, at peace, the people in his dominion neither too happy nor too sad.

5 Early in the morning of the first day of the first week of the second month of the new year, the Emperor Yuan was sipping tea and fanning himself against a warm breeze when a servant ran across the scarlet and blue garden tiles, calling, 'Oh, Emperor, Emperor, a miracle!'

'Yes,' said the Emperor, 'the air *is* sweet this morning.'

'No, no, a miracle!' said the servant, bowing quickly.

10 'And this tea is good in my mouth, surely that is a miracle.'

'No, no, Your Excellency.'

'Let me guess then – the sun has risen and a new day is upon us. Or the sea is blue. *That* now is the finest of all miracles.'

'Excellency, a man is flying!'

15 'What?' The Emperor stopped his fan.

'I saw him in the air, a man flying with wings. I heard a voice call out of the sky, and when I looked up there he was, a dragon in the heavens with a man in its mouth, a dragon of paper and bamboo, coloured like the sun and the grass.'

20 'It is early,' said the Emperor, 'and you have just wakened from a dream.'

'It is early, but I have seen what I have seen! Come, and you will see it too.'

'Sit down with me here,' said the Emperor. 'Drink some tea. It must be a strange thing, if it is true, to see a man fly. You must have time to think of it, even as I must have time to prepare myself for the sight.'

25 They drank tea.

'Please,' said the servant at last, 'or he will be gone'.

The Emperor rose thoughtfully. 'Now you may show me what you have seen.'

They walked into a garden, across a meadow of grass, over a small bridge, 30 through a grove of trees, and up a tiny hill.

'There!' said the servant.

The Emperor looked into the sky.

And in the sky, laughing so high that you could hardly hear him laugh, was a man; and the man was clothed in bright papers and reeds to make wings 35 and a beautiful yellow tail, and he was soaring all about like the largest bird in a universe of birds, like a new dragon in a land of ancient dragons. The man called down to them from high in the cool winds of the morning. 'I fly, I fly!'

The servant waved to him. 'Yes, yes!'

The Emperor Yuan did not move. Instead he looked at the Great Wall of 40 China now taking shape out of the farthest mist in the green hills, that splendid snake of stones which writhed with majesty across the entire land. The wonderful wall which had protected them for a timeless time from enemy hordes and preserved peace for years without number. He saw the town, nestled to itself by a river and a road and a hill, beginning to waken.

45   'Tell me,' he said to his servant, 'has anyone else seen this flying man?'

'I am the only one, Excellency,' said the servant, smiling at the sky, waving.

The Emperor glanced in all directions while the flying man soared down the morning wind. He saw a farmer, early in his fields, watching the sky, and he noted where the farmer stood.

50   The flying man alit with a rustle of paper and a creak of bamboo reeds. He came proudly to the Emperor, clumsy in his rig, at last bowing before the old man.

'What have you done?' demanded the Emperor.

'I have flown in the sky, Your Excellency,' replied the man.

55   'What *have* you done?' said the Emperor again.

'I have just told you!' cried the flyer.

'You have told me nothing at all.' The Emperor reached out a thin hand to touch the pretty paper and the birdlike keel of the apparatus. It smelled cool, of the wind.

60   'Is it not beautiful, Excellency?'

'Yes, too beautiful.'

'It is the only one in the world!' smiled the man. 'And I am the inventor.'

'The *only* one in the world?'

'I swear it!'

65   'Who else knows of this?'

'No one. Not even my wife, who would think me mad with the sun. She thought I was making a kite. I rose in the night and walked to the cliffs far away. And when the morning breezes blew and the sun rose, I gathered my courage, Excellency, and leaped from the cliff. I flew! But my wife does not

70 know of it.'

'Well for her, then,' said the Emperor. 'Come along.'

They walked back to the great house. The sun was full in the sky now, and the smell of the grass was refreshing. The Emperor, the servant, and the flyer paused within the huge garden.

75   The Emperor clapped his hands. 'Ho, guards!'

The guards came running.

'Hold this man.'

The guards seized the flyer.

'Call the executioner,' said the Emperor.

80   'What's this!' cried the flyer, bewildered. 'What have I done?' He began to weep, so that the beautiful paper apparatus rustled.

The executioner came running with a sharp silver axe. He stood with his naked, large-muscled arms ready, his face covered with a serene white mask.

'One moment,' said the Emperor. He turned to a nearby table upon which

85 sat a machine that he had himself created. The Emperor took a tiny gold key from his own neck. He fitted this key to the tiny, delicate machine and wound it up. Then he set the machine going.

The machine was a garden of metal and jewels. Set in motion, birds sang in tiny metal trees, wolves walked through miniature forests, and tiny people ran

90 in and out of the sun and shadow, fanning themselves with miniature fans, listening to the tiny emerald birds, and standing by impossibly small but tinkling fountains.

'Is *it* not beautiful?' said the Emperor. 'If you asked me what I have done

here, I could answer you well. I have made forests murmur. I have set people
95 to walking in this woodland, enjoying the leaves and shadows and songs. That
is what I have done.'

'But, oh, Emperor!' pleaded the flyer, on his knees, the tears pouring down
his face. 'I have done a similar thing! I have found beauty. I have flown on the
morning wind. I have looked down on all the sleeping houses and gardens. I
100 have smelled the sea and even *seen* it, beyond the hills, from my high place.
And I have soared like a bird; oh, I cannot say how beautiful it is up there, in
the sky, with the wind about me, the wind blowing me here like a feather,
there like a fan, the way the sky smells in the morning! And how free one
feels! *That* is beautiful, Emperor, that is beautiful too!'

105 'There are times,' said the Emperor, sadly, 'when one must lose a little
beauty if one is to keep what little beauty one already has. I do not fear you,
yourself, but I fear another man.'

'What man?'

'Some other man who, seeing you, will build a thing of bright paper and
110 bamboo like this. But the other man will have an evil face and evil heart, and
the beauty will be gone. It is this man I fear.'

'Why? Why?'

'Who is to say that some day just such a man, in just such an apparatus of
paper and reed, might not fly in the sky and drop huge stones upon the Great
115 Wall of China?' said the Emperor.

No one moved or said a word.

'Off with his head,' said the Emperor.

The executioner whirled his silver axe.

From *The Flying Machine* by Ray Bradbury

ENGLISH: PAPER 1 Section A

Questions

Answer question 1 and question 2.

Refer to words and phrases in the passage to support your ideas.

1 The Emperor is not pleased that one of his subjects has made a flying machine.

How does Ray Bradbury (the writer) **bring out the Emperor's feelings about the flyer and his machine?**

In your answer you should comment on:

- how the Emperor reacts to his servant's news in lines 6 to 32;
- what the Emperor says to the flyer and the way in which he says it (lines 53 to 116);
- why the Emperor finally has the flyer put to death.

10

2 During the passage, the flyer's feelings change from one extreme to the other. Show how, and say why, they do so.

8

TOTAL

ENGLISH: PAPER 1 Section A
Advice for answering

Timing

- In the test, you need to spend a total of 30–35 minutes answering Section A. Allow yourself up to 20 minutes on Question 1 and up to 15 minutes on Question 2.

- When practising the questions in this book, you can give yourself an extra ten minutes on each. The more you practise, the quicker you will become.

Preparing for Question 1

- Note that there are 10 marks for this question. In your answer, aim to make about the same number of points as there are marks available.

- Look carefully at Question 1. Pay particular attention to the instruction: 'In your answer you should comment on ...'. These three 'prompts' are your lifeline. They tell you what the examiners *require* (not 'advise') you to include in your answer.

Re-reading and underlining

- Having read the passage before the test began, in the 15 minutes' reading time, you already know in some detail what it is about. Now spend 5 minutes *re-reading* it, word for word, pencil in hand.

- Every time you find a point which you think 'you should comment on', underline it. Go through the whole passage doing this. As yet, write nothing on your answer paper.

Writing up the answer

- You now have 15 minutes to write your answer. Remember that it must contain as many different points as you can make.

- Write in sentences, not in note form. Don't waste a single word. You must never repeat something you have already written.

- It is helpful to examiners if you write your answer in paragraphs. A good way of doing this is to base one paragraph on each of the three 'prompts', making three paragraphs in all.

- You will win more marks if you quote single words and short phrases from the passage to back up the points you make.

Answering Question 2

- Spend up to 15 minutes on this. Follow exactly the same advice as that given above for Question 1 (except for underlining - this time use a pen or different coloured pencil).

Answers

Question 1

Examiners do not use a 'point by point' mark scheme, and it is quite common for two answers which gain the same mark to include different points. Some points are more difficult than others for pupils to spot. It is also unrealistic to expect any candidate, however good, to cover everything that could possibly be said. Therefore, an answer is marked according to the examiner's *overall impression of how well the passage has been understood*.

The best way to mark your child's answer is to measure its content against the mark scheme below, which incorporates the full 10 marks available. Compare the points in it with those your child has made.

Ideally, you should mark with your child beside you and discuss the mark scheme together. Bear in mind that there are many ways of expressing the same point. As long as the point is made *clearly*, it should be given credit. It is not the aim to imitate the exact vocabulary used in the mark scheme.

After checking your child's answer against the mark scheme, use your discretion to arrive at a fair and accurate score out of 10. Then decide where it fits best onto the following scale:

Mark 9 or 10:	*Exceptional performance*	(Above Level 7)
Mark 7 or 8:	*Well above average*	(Level 7)
Mark 5 or 6:	*Above average*	(Level 6)
Mark 3 or 4:	*Average/below average*	(Level 5)
Mark 1 or 2:	*Well below average*	(Level 4 or below)

It will be of great benefit for you to attempt this task yourself before marking your child's answer. Doing so will help you to become familiar with the details of the passage. This in turn will make it much easier for you to use the mark scheme confidently and quickly.

The instructions for Question 1 tell pupils to 'Refer to words and phrases in the passage to support your ideas'. In a good answer, key points made should be both **stated** *and* **illustrated by brief quotation**. Line-references are included in the mark scheme to show where such quotations would gain credit.

- The Emperor is shown to be (a) concerned and (b) displeased by what his servant tells him about the flying machine. This is brought out in the following ways:

  - at first, he does not believe - or want to believe - what the servant tells him (lines 7–15)

  - he is reluctant to see the flying machine and puts off doing so for as long as possible (lines 20–28)

  - he does not wave a greeting to the flyer - instead, he looks anxiously at the Great Wall (line 39)

  - he is interested in finding out exactly who knows about the flying machine, the first hint that he considers it to be dangerous (lines 45–71)

- his lack of enthusiasm for the flying machine is contrasted with the servant's great excitement about it

● When talking to the flyer, the Emperor is shown to be (a) upset and (b) angry about the new invention. This is brought out in the following ways:

- his first words to the flyer are spoken sternly, as if, in making the flying machine, he has committed a crime (lines 53–57)

- he is troubled that the flyer, unlike himself, cannot see that his invention could be dangerous (lines 106–108)

- he now becomes anxious to ensure that the invention will remain a secret (lines 66 & 70)

- he orders the flyer to be kept under armed guard and calls for the executioner (lines 77 & 118)

● The Emperor is shown to be aware of how destructive the flying machine could be if it fell into the wrong hands. This is brought out in the following ways:

- he explains to the flyer that something which seems beautiful can be highly dangerous, unlike his own mechanical 'garden' to which he alone keeps the key (lines 88–96)

- he says that evil men in the future may use the flying machine to attack China, turning a thing of beauty into a weapon of war and destruction (lines 109–111 & lines 114–116)

- reluctantly, he has the flyer - and presumably the farmer and the servant - put to death; the flyer's invention will die with him and there will be no risk of it falling into 'evil' hands

Question 2

Please refer back to the detailed guidance for marking on page 11. The marking procedure is the same, except for the equivalences between marks and grade levels which are:

Mark 8:	*Exceptional performance*	(Above Level 7)
Mark 6–7:	*Well above average*	(Level 7)
Mark 5:	*Above average*	(Level 6)
Mark 3– 4:	*Average/below average*	(Level 5)
Mark 1– 2:	*Well below average*	(Level 4 or below)

● The flyer's feelings change in the following ways:

- at first, he is excited and triumphant that his flying machine works (lines 54 and 60)

- when he lands, the flyer feels proud of himself and expects praise from the Emperor (lines 62–64)

- he becomes boastful about his achievement, trying to impress the Emperor with its importance (lines 67–69)

- he becomes incredulous and distressed when the guards are sent for (lines 80–81)

- he desperately tries to save his life by arguing that to fly is to experience true beauty and freedom (lines 97–104).

- The reasons why the flyer's feelings change are:

  - at first, he is exhilarated by his own success and thinks he will become famous

  - after landing, he starts to see that the Emperor is displeased with him, though he doesn't know why

  - he finally realises, with horror, that his 'reward' for being a pioneer of flight is to be death rather than everlasting fame

If you are disappointed by your child's marks so far ...

Points to bear in mind

- S/he may not yet have practised this kind of question in school very frequently. As the test approaches, 'mock' questions, with specific advice on how to tackle them, are likely to be rehearsed more.

- Think of the last time *you* worked in test conditions under the pressure of time and high expectation. Do you consider that you did full justice to your abilities? If not, why not? Share this with your child.

- A mark equating to Level 5 is currently the national norm. A mark equating to Level 6 is above average.

Strategies for improvement

- Be patient and remain supportive. No one improves their confidence or competence by feeling that they have 'failed'.

- Together with your child, make a list of no more than three 'targets' for improvement next time. These may include:

  - making better use of the 15-minute reading time before the test begins. Skim-reading alone is of limited use. It is necessary to read the passage twice, slowly, and with complete attention.

  - making a greater variety of points. Bear in mind that there are more different points in the answer than there are marks available.

  - making sure that, whenever possible, a statement in the answer is backed up by quotation, however brief.

  - making the whole answer longer, and setting it out in paragraphs which link up with the Question 'prompts'.

  - making sure that points made in answer to Question 1 neither overlap with, nor repeat, points made in answer to Question 2.

  - making a determined effort to think/write for the *whole* 30–35 minutes. Tests in English make more demands on mental stamina than any other subject. They must be 'attacked'.

- Children rarely increase their motivation for tests by having their work compared with that of others - for 'better' or for 'worse'. Avoid distracting your child in this way. Concentrate exclusively on the personal targets you have identified for improvement.

Read the leaflet on this page and the next. Then answer question 3.

Think of the planet Earth as a 46 year old...

The Earth is thought to be around 4,600 million years old, an almost inconceivable time-span. For the moment, think of it as someone in middle age, 46 years old.

This person is a late developer. Nothing at all is known about their first seven years and only sketchy information exists until about the next 35 years. It is only at the age of 42 that the Earth began to flower.

Dinosaurs and the great reptiles did not appear until a year ago, when this planet reached 45. Mammals arrived only eight months ago. In the middle of last week, human-like apes evolved into ape-like humans, and at the weekend the last ice age enveloped the earth.

Modern humans have been around for four hours. During the last hour we discovered agriculture. The industrial revolution began just a minute ago. During those sixty seconds of biological time, humans have made a rubbish tip of Paradise.

We have caused the extinction of many hundreds of species of animals, many of which have been here longer than us, and ransacked the planet for fuel. Now we stand, like brutish infants, gloating over this meteoric rise to ascendancy, poised on the brink of the final mass extinction and of effectively destroying this oasis of life in the solar system.

GREENPEACE

Greenpeace, Canonbury Villas, London N1 2PN

How far should we go to protect the planet?

GREENPEACE

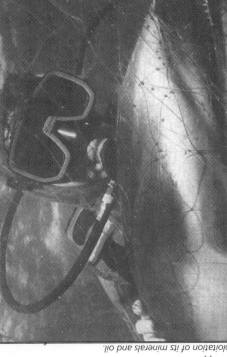

Greenpeace – making a world of difference

"We can make a difference." That's the thought that inspired a handful of North American activists when, in 1971, they sailed their small boat into a US atomic test zone off Amchitka, Alaska. They believed that you should stand up for what you believe in, however formidable the challenge and however small your voice. So Greenpeace was born.

The following successes, won over the last two decades give us all hope for the future. Without Greenpeace, how many of these battles would have been won?

- *Restored* Antarctica to its status as the last wilderness continent after an eight year campaign which consumed half our funds.
- *Helped* establish a whale sanctuary in the Southern Ocean, protecting the great whales from commercial whaling all round Antarctica.
- *Revolutionised* the refrigeration industry with the introduction of climate and ozone friendly 'greenfreeze' technology.
- *Ended* large scale driftnetting which once stripped our oceans bare.
- *Stopped* the killing of baby seals for commercial gain.
- *Alerted* governments to the alarming rise in children's asthma caused by car exhaust emissions.
- *Persuaded* the European community to reduce pollution in the North Sea including a ban on the UK dumping of industrial waste.
- *Campaigned* internationally for a ban on ozone destroying chemicals winning an agreement to phase out CFCs in Europe.

Following our protests Antarctica is now safe from exploitation of its minerals and oil.

Our diver examines a dolphin indiscriminately slaughtered in a driftnet kilometres long. Large scale driftnetting is now outlawed.

So how far will you go to save the planet?

Now we're calling on your support. As we've proved, the voice of the individual matters. The breadth and depth of our supporters' commitment allows us to act. And we totally depend on them financially. To retain our independence we never accept funds from governments or corporations, leaving us free to target whoever is at fault. Neither are we affiliated to any political organisation.

Thinking about the state of the world today can be depressing, but *you* can make a difference. Return the form today and make sure your voice is heard in a growing worldwide protest. Add your voice to ours.

We invite you to join us and save the natural world

Questions

3 *Now answer question 3 below.*

The Greenpeace organisation uses this leaflet to tell people about the work it does and to ask for their support.

In what ways does the leaflet try to persuade people to 'save the natural world' by joining Greenpeace?

In your answer your should comment on:
- the choice of pictures and the effects they have;
- the layout of the leaflet, including headings;
- the way language is used to affect the reader's feelings;
- whether the leaflet would succeed in persuading *you* to become a member.

Advice for answering

Timing

In the test, you need to spend about 20 minutes answering Section B. This seems quite a short time. However, you will know the passage fairly well from the 15-minute reading time allowed before your 'answering time' begins.

Making brief notes

Look in turn at each of the four 'prompts' which tell you what to comment on. Try to think of at least *three* points for each. Jot these down very quickly in note-form: short phrases or even single words will do.

Writing up the answer

Refer back to page 10. Follow the advice you find there (except for 'three paragraphs' read 'four'). Since you have less time, your paragraphs will be briefer than for Section A.

10

Answers

Question 3

Please refer back to the detailed guidance for marking on page 11. The marking procedure is the same as for Section A, Question 1, including the correspondence between marks out of 10 and a grade.

The mark scheme below incorporates the full 10 marks available.

- **Choice of pictures.** They show that Greenpeace members:

    (a) are brave / prepared to risk their lives for their cause
    (b) care for wildlife all over the world, however far-flung (e.g. Antarctica, Alaska) and are a truly global organisation
    (c) have a close personal concern for endangered animals
    (d) use modern equipment ('our diver') to help them in their work
    (e) care deeply about the *whole* of the planet Earth.

- **Layout and headings.** The general layout is designed:

    (a) to show the wide variety of Greenpeace's activities
    (b) in ordered 'sections' (i.e. the panels) - the reader is led from being shocked into understanding the urgent plight of the planet, to feeling glad that Greenpeace has been taking action for a long time, to making the decision to join them.
    (c) The headings highlight the 'sectioned' format. They are also skilfully worded, emphasising 'world' and 'planet' by repetition, and using puns to influence the reader ('How *far* should we go?'... 'How *far* will *you* go?' / 'Making a *world* of difference').

- **Language used to persuade.** Examples and explanations of persuasive language include:

    (a) the use of puns and word-play in the headings (see (c) above)
    (b) the extended comparison between the age of the earth and an adult in middle age. This brings the 'inconceivable' time-span of 4,600 million years within the scope of the reader's experience and imagination ('modern humans have been around for four hours', etc.)
    (c) the use of 'shock tactic' language ('humans have made a rubbish tip of paradise' … 'Now we stand, like brutish infants, poised on the brink of the final mass extinction'). This heightened or exaggerated style is meant to jolt the reader into realising how like irresponsible vandals human beings can be.
    (d) a direct appeal to the reader in the last section of the leaflet, where the words 'you' and 'your' are used six times in as many sentences. This is intended to make readers feel that they have a duty to join Greenpeace and that every new member takes on a *personal* responsibility for 'saving the natural world'.

- **Would the leaflet persuade *you* to become a member?**

    Give credit for any point which is (a) supported by reference to particular parts of the leaflet and (b) which has not been made elsewhere in the answer.

*Choose **one** of the following questions.*

4 *Either*

(a) Some part of the countryside, or a species of animal that you care about, is under threat.

Write an article for a newspaper explaining why the place or the animal in question should be saved.

In your writing you could:
- explain where the threat is coming from;
- say why urgent action needs to be taken;
- put forward your ideas on the best way to take such action;
- appeal to the newspaper's readers to support your ideas and suggestions.

Or

(b) **Write about someone who has an adventure which tests his/her nerve and courage to the full.**

In your writing you could:
- write about a real or imaginary event;
- try to build up a feeling of suspense or danger.

Or

(c) Many inventions of the twentieth century have made life better for everybody. It might be said that some inventions have made life worse.

Write about one or more twentieth century inventions that you think fall into either of these categories.

In your writing you could:
- describe the effects on people's lives of the invention(s) you choose;
- weigh up the benefits and problems they bring with them;
- give careful reasons for the opinions you hold.

32

TOTAL

Question 4

Unlike Questions 1, 2 and 3, Question 4 is marked for *overall impression*. The content and the style/accuracy of the writing are taken equally into account.

Consequently, there is no 'step by step' mark scheme. Assigning a mark to an answer works (a) by checking it against the Assessment Objectives to see how well the pupil has met them and (b) by using a 'best fit' procedure to find an appropriate Level for the answer.

Assessment objectives

You should, on an impression basis, assess your child's answer by judging how well it matches the following criteria:

- communicates ideas clearly to the reader;
- makes use of a style suitable to the written task;
- organises the subject matter in a way appropriate to the chosen form (i.e. story, article, argument, etc.);
- shapes and develops the subject matter using paragraphs, grammar and punctuation to convey meaning;
- makes use of words precisely and imaginatively, spelling them correctly;
- is written neatly and legibly.

Best-fit criteria

You should use the two sets of criteria below to 'place' your child's answer in a grade Level band between 4– and 7+.

Level 4: The pupils' ideas are generally clear. There is some attempt to organise them into a suitable form. Pupils are beginning to choose words effectively. There is some use of grammatically correct sentences. Punctuation to mark sentences is mostly used accurately and pupils are beginning to use punctuation within the sentence. Spelling of simple and common longer words is generally accurate. Handwriting is mostly clear and legible.

Level 6: The pupils' writing is interesting in parts, using a suitable style for the task. The quality of the writing is enhanced by a varied vocabulary, a range of simple and complex sentences, and appropriate paragraphing. A range of punctuation is usually used correctly to clarify meaning. Spelling is usually accurate. Handwriting is in a fluent and legible form.

After checking your child's answer against the mark scheme above, decide where it best fits on the following scale:

Mark 30–32:	*Exceptional performance*	(Above Level 7)
Mark 24–29:	*Well above average*	(Level 7)
Mark 18–23:	*Above average/average*	(Level 6)
Mark 13–17:	*Average/below average*	(Level 5)
Mark 7–12:	*Well below average*	(Level 4 or below)

Preparing for the test

Read through the whole of this section now, slowly and without stopping. It will help you do your best work in Paper 2 of the test.

When you go on to practise writing answers on Shakespeare (see pages 23 to 39 of this book), keep referring back to this section. You will need to remind yourself of the advice it gives.

Preparing for Paper 2 in school

- During Year 9, you'll have a lot of lessons (too many, you might think!) on the Shakespeare play chosen by your teachers: *Julius Caesar* **or** *A Midsummer Night's Dream* **or** *Romeo and Juliet*. How well you do in the test depends enormously on how well you understand and remember what you hear, say and write in these lessons, and/or for homework.

    This makes it different from Paper 1, where you cannot prepare for the content of the test. So, if you really find yourself struggling to understand your Shakespeare lessons, talk about it to your teacher - or ask your parents to do so.

- The examiners expect you to know the whole of whichever Shakespeare play you are doing. There are 5 Acts, each of them made up of a number of different Scenes.

    In the test, you are likely to be questioned on just **one** Scene. However, to write a really good answer you often need to refer to other parts of the play. So it's risky to know only a couple of Scenes inside out and others hardly at all.

- When you take the test, you will be given a booklet with the Scene(s) on which you have to answer printed in it. There are *two* Scenes from which you can choose. This gives you a bit of room for manoeuvre - but not much.

    You are not allowed to take anything into the test to help you answer, except your memory. This is by far and away your most important 'aid'.

What are the questions like?

Look ahead to pages 23, 28 and 34. You will see examples of a typical question on each of the three Shakespeare plays set for the test you will take. They are identical to questions that have been asked by the examiners in recent years. Read very carefully the question on 'your' play.

How to plan your answer

- A good answer will be well-planned. A poor answer will not. So, out of the 1¼ hours allowed, spend *at least* 15 minutes thinking, underlining parts of the Scene in your booklet, and jotting ideas on your answer paper before you start to write. (Cross out any 'plan' work at the end of the test.)

- The golden rule is: write what the examiners ask you to write, not what *you* decide you'd rather do. To make sure you write 'to task', you will find it helpful to plan in the following way:

    - Take each of the examiners' 'prompts' in turn (e.g. 'Before you begin to write you should think about the different ways the Friar reacts to Romeo's moods / the language the Friar uses', etc). Number these 1, 2, 3 etc. on your question paper.

    - Now read through the Scene in your booklet slowly, pencil in hand. Underline any lines, phrases, or even single words, which you think connect up to each

20

numbered 'prompt'. In the margin, write the appropriate number opposite each underlining.

- Next, organise your thoughts on paper into an essay plan, still using pencil. It works well to 'collect' together your Number 1 ideas into a cluster for the first part of the essay. Do the same with your Number 2, Number 3, Number 4 ideas until you have gone through all the 'prompts'.

- The last stage of planning is to decide which quotations you will use to back up what you say in your answer. Examiners give marks generously if you quote in the right way, which is: *to 'prove', or illustrate, every main point you make with a suitable line or phrase which Shakespeare wrote*. So, using a pen, underline in your booklet - usually over a pencilled underlining - the parts of the Scene that you are going to quote. These *must* be clearly linked to the points you have already planned to make.

● You are now ready to write your own answer. You will have between 45 and 60 minutes - long enough for you to do as well as you possibly can.

Writing your answer

● **Length.** Your answer paper is A4 size. Most good answers are between three and four sides long.

● **Paragraphs.** You will win marks for using paragraphs (a) to show when you move on from one main point to the next and (b) to help the examiner to follow the stages of your answer easily. You will lose marks (a) for not using paragraphs at all and (b) for changing paragraphs too often - for example, every sentence or two.

● **Using quotations.** There is no single or 'right' way to set out your quotations. However, the two methods shown below are those most favoured by examiners. Note the use of double quotation marks, as when you write speech in a story.

(a) Antony speaks very cleverly, never saying anything about Brutus that is outwardly critical:

"Yet Brutus is an honourable man."

This is an excellent tactic. Antony uses more and more sarcasm about Brutus without putting his real feelings into plain words, therefore not risking being stopped from speaking but still letting the crowd know what he really thinks.

(b) Paris is very blunt when he talks to Juliet. His first words to her are: "Happily met, my lady and my wife". He hasn't even proposed to her yet. He has "talked little of love / For Venus smiles not in a house of tears".

● **Style of writing.** The sections below give you guidance about this.

How is your answer marked?

Examiners mark your answer twice. First you are given a grade for *Understanding and Response*. Then you are given a second grade for *Written Expression*. These two grades are not 'averaged out'. It is possible to get, say, a grade 6 for Understanding and Response and a grade 4 for Written Expression. Examiners award the two grades to your answer by using the following yardsticks.

● **Understanding and Response.** The tasks in this paper assess pupils' ability to understand and respond to:

- Shakespeare's presentation of ideas;

- the motivation and behaviour of the characters;

- the development of plot;

- the language of the scenes;
- the presentation of the scenes on stage.

● **Written Expression.** Also assessed on this paper will be your ability to:

- write in a style appropriate to the task;
- organise writing clearly, using paragraphs where appropriate;
- use grammatical structures and vocabulary suitable for the clear and precise expression of meaning;
- use a variety of sentence structures;
- use accurate punctuation and spelling;
- write clearly and legibly.

No two people write in the same way. Examiners do not have a 'perfect style' in mind when they assess your written expression. They will give you high marks if the way you write is:

- straightforward and to the point. If you ramble, repeat yourself or beat about the bush, expect to be penalised.

- well-constructed. This means that each sentence should lead clearly on to the next and that there must be obvious links between your paragraphs.

- personal and lively. Examiners are interested to see if you can write in an *individual* way, not like a robot or a dictionary. You should try to avoid using slang or 'showing off' how many big words you know.

- accurate. You will be well rewarded for correct spelling (including the names of characters in the play), correct use of full-stops, correct use of capital letters, and for handwriting that is easy to read.

Julius Caeser

Act 1 Scene ii, lines 1–184

In this scene, Brutus wonders whether Caesar is becoming too powerful for the good of Rome.

What happens in the scene to persuade Brutus to join the conspiracy to murder Caesar?

Before you begin to write you should think about:

- Caesar's words and actions in the first part of the scene;

- the events happening off-stage in the market-place;

- what Cassius says to turn Brutus against Caesar;

- Cassius's skill with words;

- Brutus's sense of responsibility towards Rome and its people.

Scene II. – Rome. A Public Place.

Enter, in procession, with music, CAESAR; ANTONY, for the course; CALPHURNIA, PORTIA, DECIUS, CICERO, BRUTUS, CASSIUS and CASCA; a great crowd following, among them a Soothsayer.

CAESAR.	Calphurnia!	
CASCA.	Peace, ho! Caesar speaks.	[Music ceases.
CAESAR.	Calphurnia!	
CALPHURNIA.	Here, my lord.	
CAESAR.	Stand you directly in Antonius' way When he doth run his course. Antonius!	
ANTONY.	Caesar, my lord.	
CAESAR.	Forget not, in your speed, Antonius, To touch Calphurnia; for our elders say, The barren, touched in this holy chase, Shake off their sterile curse.	10
ANTONY.	I shall remember: When Caesar says 'Do this', it is perform'd.	
CAESAR.	Set on; and leave no ceremony out.	[Music.
SOOTHSAYER.	Caesar!	
CAESAR.	Ha! Who calls?	
CASCA.	Bid every noise be still: peace yet again!	
		[Music ceases.
CAESAR.	Who is it in the press that calls on me? I hear a tongue, shriller than all the music, Cry 'Caesar'. Speak; Caesar is turn'd to hear.	20
SOOTHSAYER.	Beware the ides of March.	
CAESAR.	What man is that?	
BRUTUS.	A soothsayer bids you beware the ides of March.	
CAESAR.	Set him before me; let me see his face.	
CASSIUS.	Fellow, come from the throng; look upon Caesar.	
CAESAR.	What sayst thou to me now? Speak once again.	
SOOTHSAYER.	Beware the ides of March.	
CAESAR.	He is a dreamer; let us leave him: pass.	

[Sennet. Exeunt all but Brutus and Cassius.

CASSIUS.	Will you go see the order of the course?	
BRUTUS.	Not I.	30
CASSIUS.	I pray you, do.	
BRUTUS.	I am not gamesome: I do lack some part	
	Of that quick spirit that is in Antony.	
	Let me not hinder, Cassius, your desires;	
	I'll leave you.	
CASSIUS.	Brutus, I do observe you now of late:	
	I have not from your eyes that gentleness	
	And show of love as I was wont to have:	
	You bear too stubborn and too strange a hand	
	Over your friend that loves you.	40
BRUTUS.	Cassius,	
	Be no deceiv'd: if I have veil'd my look,	
	I turn the trouble of my countenance	
	Merely upon myself. Vexed I am	
	Of late with passions of some difference,	
	Conceptions only proper to myself,	
	Which give some soil perhaps to my behaviours;	
	But let not therefore my good friends be griev'd, –	
	Among which number, Cassius, be you one, –	
	Nor construe any further my neglect,	50
	Than that poor Brutus, with himself at war,	
	Forgets the shows of love to other men.	
CASSIUS.	Then, Brutus, I have much mistook your passion;	
	By means whereof this breast of mine hath buried	
	Thoughts of great value, worthy cogitations.	
	Tell me, good Brutus, can you see your face?	
BRUTUS.	No, Cassius; for the eye sees not itself,	
	But by reflection, by some other things.	
CASSIUS.	'Tis just:	
	And it is very much lamented, Brutus,	60
	That you have no such mirrors as will turn	
	Your hidden worthiness into your eye,	
	That you might see your shadow. I have heard,	
	Where many of the best respect in Rome, –	
	Except immortal Caesar, – speaking of Brutus,	
	And groaning underneath this age's yoke,	
	Have wish'd that noble Brutus had his eyes.	
BRUTUS.	Into what dangers would you lead me, Cassius,	
	That you would have me seek into myself	
	For that which is not in me?	70
CASSIUS.	Therefore, good Brutus, be prepar'd to hear;	
	And, since you know you cannot see yourself	
	So well as by reflection, I, your glass,	
	Will modestly discover to yourself	
	That of yourself which you yet know not of.	
	And be not jealous on me, gentle Brutus:	
	Were I a common laugher, or did use	
	To stale with ordinary oaths my love	
	To every new protester; if you know	
	That I do fawn on men and hug them hard,	80

24

And after scandal them; or if you know
That I profess myself in banqueting
To all the rout, then hold me dangerous.   [*Flourish and shout.*

BRUTUS.   What means this shouting? I do fear, the people
Choose Caesar for their king.

CASSIUS.   Ay, do you fear it?
Then must I think you would not have it so

BRUTUS.   I would not, Cassius; yet I love him well.
But wherefore do you hold me here so long?
What is it that you would impart to me?   90
If it be aught toward the general good,
Set honour in one eye and death i' the other,
And I will look on both indifferently;
For let the gods so speed me as I love
The name of honour more than I fear death.

CASSIUS.   I know that virtue to be in you, Brutus,
As well as I do know your outward favour.
Well, honour is the subject of my story.
I cannot tell what you and other men
Think of this life; but, for my single self,   100
I had as lief not be as live to be
In awe of such a thing as I myself.
I was born free as Caesar; so were you:
We both have fed as well, and we can both
Endure the winter's cold as well as he:
For once, upon a raw and gusty day,
The troubled Tiber chafing with her shores,
Caesar said to me, 'Dar'st thou, Cassius, now
Leap in with me into this angry flood,
And swim to yonder point?' Upon the word,   110
Accoutred as I was, I plunged in
And bade him follow; so indeed he did.
The torrent roar'd, and we did buffet it
With lusty sinews, throwing it aside
And stemming it with hearts of controversy;
But ere we could arrive the point propos'd,
Caesar cried, 'Help me, Cassius, or I sink!'
I, as Aeneas, our great ancestor,
Did from the flames of Troy upon his shoulder
The old Anchises bear, so from the waves of Tiber   120
Did I the tired Caesar. And this man
Is now become a god, and Cassius is
A wretched creature and must bend his body
If Caesar carelessly but nod on him.
He had a fever when he was in Spain,
And when the fit was on him, I did mark
How he did shake; 'tis true, this god did shake;
His coward lips did from their colour fly,
And that same eye whose bend doth awe the world
Did lose his lustre; I did hear him groan;   130
Ay, and that tongue of his that bade the Romans
Mark him and write his speeches in their books,

Alas! it cried, 'Give me some drink, Titinius,'
As a sick girl. Ye gods, it doth amaze me,
A man of such a feeble temper should
So get the start of the majestic world,
And bear the palm alone.   [Flourish. Shout.

BRUTUS.   Another general shout!
I do believe that these applauses are
For some new honours that are heaped on Caesar.   140

CASSIUS.   Why, man, he doth bestride the narrow world
Like a Colossus; and we petty men
Walk under his huge legs, and peep about
To find ourselves dishonourable graves.
Men at some time are masters of their fates:
The fault, dear Brutus, is not in our stars,
But in ourselves, that we are underlings.
Brutus and Caesar: what should be in that 'Caesar'?
Why should that name be sounded more than yours?
Write them together, yours is as fair a name;   150
Sound them, it doth become the mouth as well;
Weigh them, it is as heavy; conjure with 'em,
'Brutus' will start a spirit as soon as 'Caesar'.
Now, in the names of all the gods at once,
Upon what meat doth this our Caesar feed,
That he is grown so great? Age, thou art sham'd!
Rome, thou has lost the breed of noble bloods!
When went there by an age, since the great flood,
But it was fam'd with more than with one man?
When could they say, till now, that talk'd of Rome,   160
That her wide walls encompass'd but one man?
Now is it Rome indeed and room enough,
When there is in it but one only man.
O! you and I have heard our fathers say,
There was a Brutus once that would have brook'd
The eternal devil to keep his state in Rome
As easily as a king.

BRUTUS.   That you do love me, I am nothing jealous;
What you would work me to, I have some aim:
How I have thought of this and of these times,   170
I shall recount hereafter; for this present,
I would not, so with love I might entreat you,
Be any further mov'd. What you have said
I will consider; what you have to say
I will with patience hear, and find a time
Both meet to hear and answer such high things.
Till then, my noble friend, chew upon this:
Brutus had rather be a villager
Than to repute himself a son of Rome
Under these hard conditions as this time   180
Is like to lay upon us.

CASSIUS.   I am glad
That my weak words have struck but thus much show
Of fire from Brutus.

26

ENGLISH: PAPER 2 (i)
ANSWERS: Understanding and response

Julius Caesar

There are 30 marks available for this section: 15 for Understanding and Response, and 15 for Written Expression. The mark-scheme below is for Understanding and Response, and incorporates the full 15 marks available. Please see page 40 for detailed comments on how to assess written expression.

After checking your child's answer against the mark scheme, decide where it best fits onto the following scale:

Mark 13 – 15:	*Exceptional performance*	(Above Level 7)
Mark 10 – 12:	*Well above average*	(Level 7)
Mark 8 – 9:	*Above average*	(Level 6)
Mark 6 – 7:	*Average/below average*	(Level 5)
Mark 3 – 5:	*Well below average*	(Level 4 or below)

The answer should point out, *and* illustrate by quotation, the following:

- **Caesar's words and actions.** (a) He shows towering arrogance. (b) He assumes that his every word will be obeyed. (c) His tone is commanding and authoritarian. (d) He expects everyone to defer to him (e.g. Antony's comment 'When Caesar says "Do this", it is performed').

- **Events off-stage.** On two occasions a 'shout' is heard by Brutus and Cassius indicating that 'the people / Choose Caesar for their king' (lines 83 and 137). In each case, Brutus voices his anxiety - and therefore his unease - about Caesar becoming too powerful.

- **Cassius's persuasion of Brutus.** (a) He hints that many respected Romans who love their country think Brutus is turning a blind eye to Caesar's growing tyranny (lines 63–67). (b) He describes how he once saved Caesar from drowning, to show Brutus that 'this man' is an ordinary human being, not 'a god'. (c) For the same reason, he belittles Caesar by recalling how he 'did shake' and showed cowardice. (d) He leads Brutus to think that he is not himself inferior to Caesar and so should not be cowed by him (lines 148–154). (e) He tells Brutus that if Caesar becomes 'king' it will be the end of democracy in Rome, which he knows Brutus values (lines 156–163)

- **Cassius's skill with words.** (a) He cleverly flatters Brutus (line 40, line 76, lines 49–150). (b) He is increasingly sarcastic about Caesar (line 65, line 127). (c) He gradually exaggerates his picture of Caesar when he sees that his attempt to persuade Brutus is working (e.g. lines 141–143).

  (d) He is highly sensitive to Brutus's changing mood and takes his cue from it (line 86, line 140).

- **Brutus's patriotism.** (a) He says he has at heart 'the general good' and that he loves 'the name of honour'. (b) As 'a son of Rome', he swears not to let 'these hard conditions' drive freedom from the state.

Act 1 Scene i, lines 1–227

In this scene, Hermia and Lysander plan to run away together to get married.

You are Hermia. Write secretly to a close friend explaining why you have decided to elope and saying what your feelings are about it.

Before you begin to write you should decide what Hermia thinks and feels about:

- her father, Egeus;
- the advice Duke Theseus gives her;
- Lysander's plan;
- what Helena tells her about Demetrius;
- the experience of being in love.

A MIDSUMMER-NIGHT'S DREAM

ACT I.

Scene I.–Athens. The Palace of Theseus.

Enter THESEUS, HIPPOLYTA, PHILOSTRATE and Attendants.

THESEUS.	Now, fair Hippolyta, our nuptial hour	
	Draws on apace: four happy days bring in	
	Another moon; but O! methinks how slow	
	This old moon wanes; she lingers my desires,	
	Like to a step-dame, or a dowager	
	Long withering out a young man's revenue.	
HIPPOLYTA.	Four days will quickly steep themselves in night;	
	Four nights will quickly dream away the time;	
	And then the moon, like to a silver bow	
	New-bent in heaven, shall behold the night	10
	Of our solemnities.	
THESEUS.	Go, Philostrate,	
	Stir up the Athenian youth to merriments;	
	Awake the pert and nimble spirit of mirth;	
	Turn melancholy forth to funerals;	
	The pale companion is not for our pomp.	[Exit PHILOSTRATE.
	Hippolyta, I woo'd thee with my sword,	
	And won thy love doing thee injuries;	
	But I will wed thee in another key,	
	With pomp, with triumph, and with revelling.	

Enter EGEUS, HERMIA, LYSANDER, and DEMETRIUS.

EGEUS.	Happy be Theseus, our renowned duke!	20
THESEUS.	Thanks, good Egeus: what's the news with thee?	
EGEUS.	Full of vexation come I, with complaint	
	Against my child, my daughter Hermia.	
	Stand forth, Demetrius. My noble lord,	
	This man hath my consent to marry her.	

Stand forth, Lysander: and, my gracious duke,
This man hath bewitch'd the bosom of my child:
Thou, thou Lysander, thou hast given her rimes,
And interchang'd love-tokens with my child;
Thou hast by moonlight at her window sung,   30
With feigning voice, verses of feigning love;
And stol'n the impression of her fantasy
With bracelets of thy hair, rings, gawds, conceits,
Knacks, trifles, nosegays, sweetmeats, messengers
Of strong prevailment in unharden'd youth;
With cunning hast thou filch'd my daughter's heart;
Turn'd her obedience, which is due to me,
To stubborn harshness. And, my gracious duke,
Be it so she will not here before your Grace
Consent to marry with Demetrius,   40
I beg the ancient privilege of Athens,
As she is mine, I may dispose of her;
Which shall be either to this gentleman,
Or to her death, according to our law
Immediately provided in that case.

THESEUS. What say you, Hermia? be advis'd, fair maid.
To you, your father should be as a god;
One that compos'd your beauties, yea and one
To whom you are but as a form in wax
By him imprinted, and within his power   50
To leave the figure or disfigure it.
Demetrius is a worthy gentleman.

HERMIA. So is Lysander.

THESEUS. In himself he is;
But, in this kind, wanting your father's voice,
The other must be held the worthier.

HERMIA. I would my father look'd but with my eyes.

THESEUS. Rather your eyes must with his judgment look.

HERMIA. I do entreat your Grace to pardon me.
I know not by what power I am made bold,   60
Nor how it may concern my modesty
In such a presence here to plead my thoughts;
But I beseech your Grace, that I may know
The worst that may befall me in this case,
If I refuse to wed Demetrius.

THESEUS. Either to die the death, or to abjure
For ever the society of men.
Therefore, fair Hermia, question your desires;
Know of your youth, examine well your blood,
Whether, if you yield not to your father's choice,   70
You can endure the livery of a nun,
For aye to be in shady cloister mew'd,
To live a barren sister all your life,
Chanting faint hymns to the cold fruitless moon.
Thrice blessed they that master so their blood,
To undergo such maiden pilgrimage;
But earthlier happy is the rose distill'd,

	Than that which withering on the virgin thorn	
	Grows, lives, and dies, in single blessedness.	
HERMIA.	So will I grow, so live, so die, my lord,	80
	Ere I will yield my virgin patent up	
	Unto his lordship, whose unwished yoke	
	My soul consents not to give sovereignty.	
THESEUS.	Take time to pause; and, by the next new moon, –	
	The sealing-day betwixt my love and me	
	For everlasting bond of fellowship, –	
	Upon that day either prepare to die	
	For disobedience to your father's will,	
	Or else to wed Demetrius, as he would;	
	Or on Diana's altar to protest	90
	For aye austerity and single life.	
DEMETRIUS.	Relent, sweet Hermia; and, Lysander, yield	
	Thy crazed title to my certain right.	
LYSANDER.	You have her father's love, Demetrius;	
	Let me have Hermia's: do you marry him.	
EGEUS.	Scornful Lysander! true, he hath my love,	
	And what is mine my love shall render him;	
	And she is mine, and all my right of her	
	I do estate unto Demetrius.	
LYSANDER.	I am, my lord, as well deriv'd as he,	100
	As well possess'd; my love is more than his;	
	My fortunes every way as fairly rank'd	
	If not with vantage, as Demetrius';	
	And, which is more than all these boasts can be,	
	I am belov'd of beauteous Hermia.	
	Why should not I then prosecute my right?	
	Demetrius, I'll avouch it to his head,	
	Made love to Nedar's daughter, Helena.	
	And won her soul; and she, sweet lady, dotes,	
	Devoutly dotes, dotes in idolatry,	110
	Upon this spotted and inconstant man.	
THESEUS.	I must confess that I have heard so much,	
	And with Demetrius thought to have spoke thereof;	
	But, being over-full of self-affairs,	
	My mind did lose it. But, Demetrius, come;	
	And come, Egeus; you shall go with me,	
	I have some private schooling for you both.	
	For you, fair Hermia, look you arm yourself	
	To fit your fancies to your father's will,	
	Or else the law of Athens yields you up,	120
	Which by no means we may extenuate,	
	To death, or to a vow of single life.	
	Come, my Hippolyta: what cheer, my love?	
	Demetrius and Egeus, go along:	
	I must employ you in some business	
	Against our nuptial, and confer with you	
	Of something nearly that concerns yourselves.	
EGEUS.	With duty and desire we follow you.	

[Exeunt THESEUS, HIPPOLYTA, EGEUS, DEMETRIUS, and train.

LYSANDER.	How now, my love! Why is your cheek so pale?	
	How chance the roses there do fade so fast?	130
HERMIA.	Belike for want of rain, which I could well	
	Beteem them from the tempest of mine eyes.	
LYSANDER.	Ay me! for aught that ever I could read,	
	Could ever hear by tale or history,	
	The course of true love never did run smooth;	
	But, either it was different in blood, –	
HERMIA.	O cross! too high to be enthrall'd to low.	
LYSANDER.	Or else misgraffed in respect of years, –	
HERMIA.	O spite! too old to be engag'd to young.	
LYSANDER.	Or else it stood upon the choice of friends, –	140
HERMIA.	O hell! to choose love by another's eye.	
LYSANDER.	Or, if there were a sympathy in choice,	
	War, death, or sickness did lay siege to it,	
	Making it momentary as a sound,	
	Swift as a shadow, short as any dream,	
	Brief as the lightning in the collied night,	
	That, in a spleen, unfolds both heaven and earth,	
	And ere a man hath power to say, 'Behold!'	
	The jaws of darkness do devour it up:	
	So quick bright things come to confusion.	150
HERMIA.	If then true lovers have been ever cross'd,	
	It stands as an edict in destiny:	
	Then let us teach our trial patience,	
	Because it is a customary cross,	
	As due to love as thoughts and dreams and sighs,	
	Wishes and tears, poor fancy's followers.	
LYSANDER.	A good persuasion: therefore, hear me, Hermia.	
	I have a widow aunt, a dowager	
	Of great revenue, and she hath no child:	
	From Athens is her house remote seven leagues:	160
	And she respects me as her only son.	
	There, gentle Hermia, may I marry thee,	
	And to that place the sharp Athenian law	
	Cannot pursue us. If thou lov'st me then,	
	Steal forth thy father's house to-morrow night,	
	And in the wood a league without the town,	
	Where I did meet thee once with Helena,	
	To do observance to a morn of May,	
	There will I stay for thee.	
HERMIA.	My good Lysander!	170
	I swear to thee by Cupid's strongest bow,	
	By his best arrow with the golden head,	
	By the simplicity of Venus' doves,	
	By that which knitteth souls and prospers loves,	
	And by that fire which burn'd the Carthage queen,	
	When the false Troyan under sail was seen,	
	By all the vows that ever men have broke, –	
	In number more than ever women spoke, –	

	In that same place thou has appointed me,	
	To-morrow truly will I meet with thee.	180
LYSANDER.	Keep promise, love. Look here comes Helena.	

Enter HELENA.

HERMIA.	God speed fair Helena! Whither away?	
HELENA.	Call you me fair? that fair again unsay.	
	Demetrius loves your fair: O happy fair!	
	Your eyes are lode-stars! and your tongue's sweet air	
	More tuneable than lark to shepherd's ear,	
	When wheat is green, when hawthorn buds appear.	
	Sickness is catching: O! were favour so,	
	Yours would I catch, fair Hermia, ere I go;	
	My ear should catch your voice, my eye your eye,	190
	My tongue should catch your tongue's sweet melody.	
	Were the world mine, Demetrius being bated,	
	The rest I'd give to be to you translated.	
	O! teach me how you look, and with what art	
	You sway the motion of Demetrius' heart.	
HERMIA.	I frown upon him, yet he loves me still.	
HELENA.	O! that your frowns would teach my smiles such skill.	
HERMIA.	I give him curses, yet he gives me love.	
HELENA.	O! that my prayers could such affection move.	
HERMIA.	The more I hate, the more he follows me.	200
HELENA.	The more I love, the more he hateth me.	
HERMIA.	His folly, Helena, is no fault of mine.	
HELENA.	None, but your beauty: would that fault were mine!	
HERMIA.	Take comfort: he no more shall see my face;	
	Lysander and myself will fly this place.	
	Before the time I did Lysander see,	
	Seem'd Athens as a paradise to me:	
	O! then, what graces in my love do dwell,	
	That he hath turn'd a heaven unto a hell.	
LYSANDER.	Helen, to you our minds we will unfold.	210
	To-morrow night, when Phœbe both behold	
	Her silver visage in the water glass,	
	Decking with liquid pearl the bladed grass, –	
	A time that lovers' flights doth still conceal, –	
	Through Athens' gates have we devis'd to steal.	
HERMIA.	And in the wood, where often you and I	
	Upon faint primrose-beds were wont to lie,	
	Emptying our bosoms of their counsel sweet,	
	There my Lysander and myself shall meet;	
	And thence from Athens turn away our eyes,	220
	To seek new friends and stranger companies.	
	Farewell sweet playfellow: pray thou for us;	
	And good luck grant thee thy Demetrius!	
	Keep word, Lysander: we must starve our sight	
	From lovers' food till morrow deep midnight.	
LYSANDER.	I will, my Hermia.– [Exit Hermia] Helena, adieu:	226
	As you on him, Demetrius dote on you!	[Exit.

ENGLISH: PAPER 2 (ii)

ANSWERS: Understanding and response

A Midsummer-Night's Dream

There are 30 marks available for this section: 15 for Understanding and Response, and 15 for Written Expression. The mark scheme below is for Understanding and Response, and incorporates the full 15 marks available. Please see page 40 for detailed comments on how to assess written expression.

After checking your child's answer against the mark scheme, decide where it best fits onto the following scale:

Mark 13 – 15:	*Exceptional performance*	(Above Level 7)
Mark 10 – 12:	*Well above average*	(Level 7)
Mark 8 – 9:	*Above average/average*	(Level 6)
Mark 6 – 7:	*Average/below average*	(Level 5)
Mark 3 – 5:	*Well below average*	(Level 4 or below)

The answer should make clear Hermia's feelings about:

- **Egeus.** (a) Anger and bitterness that he views her less as a daughter than as a possession ('As she is mine, I may dispose of her': line 42). (b) Horror that he is willing to see her dead if she goes on refusing to marry Demetrius (line 44). (c) Resentment that he thinks her so immature and shallow as to be tricked into falling in love (see lines 27–35, where he repeatedly refers to her as a 'child').

- **The Duke's advice.** (a) Alarm that he supports her father's demands (e.g. lines 66–67). (b) Disappointment that he is unmoved by the pleas of herself and Lysander, especially since he himself is in love and about to marry. (c) Some consolation that he speaks to her in a more calm, kind and understanding way than Egeus does (e.g. 'What say you, Hermia? Be advised, fair maid': line 46).

- **Lysander's plan.** (a) Relief that the plan solves all her problems at once: they can marry without Egeus's consent and, because the place is outside Athens, the law cannot touch them (lines 162–164). (b) Immense happiness: Lysander's plan confirms that he truly loves her, as she loves him (see her rapturous response, lines 170–180).

- **Helena's news about Demetrius.** (a) Sympathy with Helena, her 'sweet playfellow', who is in love with a man who scorns her (line 201). (b) Annoyance at Demetrius, whose infatuation with her beauty is both unwanted and the cause of Helena's misery (lines 196–198).

- **The experience of being in love.** Credit any points that are borne out by the text. Hermia's strongest feeling is that love is the cause of deep distress and extreme happiness, emotions which in this scene are almost simultaneous. Love is similarly perplexing in that 'The more I hate, the more he follows me' … 'The more I love, the more he hateth me'.

Romeo and Juliet

Act 3 Scene 1

Mercutio (a Montague) and Tybalt (a Capulet) are important characters in this scene.

What do you think about the way Mercutio behaves?

If you wish, you may answer the question as though you are going to direct this scene. You could begin: "As director of the play I want the audience to have strong feelings about Mercutio. For example ..."

Before you begin to write you should think about:

- Mercutio's attitude towards quarrelling with the Capulets;

- the way in which Tybalt and Mercutio speak to each other;

- why Mercutio fights with Tybalt, despite Romeo's attempt to stop him;

- how Mercutio faces up to his death;

- the importance of this scene to what happens later in the play.

ACT III.

Scene I. – Verona. A Public Place.

Enter MERCUTIO, BENVOLIO, Page, and Servants.

BENVOLIO.	I pray thee, good Mercutio, let's retire: The day is hot, the Capulets abroad, And, if we meet, we shall not 'scape a brawl; For now, these hot days, is the mad blood stirring.	
MERCUTIO.	Though art like one of those fellows that when he enters the confines of a tavern claps me his sword upon the table, and says 'God send me no need of thee!' and by the operation of the second cup draws him on the drawer, when, indeed, there is no need.	
BENVOLIO.	Am I like such a fellow?	10
MERCUTIO.	Come, come, thou art as hot a Jack in thy mood as any in Italy; and as soon moved to be moody, and as soon moody to be moved.	
BENVOLIO.	And what to?	
MERCUTIO.	Nay, an there were two such, we should have none shortly, for one would kill the other. Thou! why, thou wilt quarrel with a man that hath a hair more or a hair less in his beard than thou hast. Thou wilt quarrel with a man for cracking nuts, having no other reason but because thou hast hazel eyes. What eye, but such an eye, would spy out such a quarrel? Thy head is as full of quarrels as an egg is full of meat, and yet thy head hath been beaten as addle as an egg for quarrelling. Thou has quarrelled with a man for coughing in the street, because he hath wakened thy dog that hath lain asleep in the sun. Didst thou not fall out with a tailor for wearing his new doublet before Easter? with another, for tying his new shoes with old	20

	riband? and yet thou wilt tutor me from quarrelling!	
BENVOLIO.	An I were so apt to quarrel as thou art, any man should buy the fee-simple of my life for an hour and a quarter.	
MERCUTIO.	The fee-simple! O simple!	30
BENVOLIO.	By my head, here come the Capulets.	
MERCUTIO.	By my heel, I care not.	

Enter TYBALT, *and Others.*

TYBALT.	Follow me close, for I will speak to them. Gentlemen, good den! a word with one of you.	
MERCUTIO.	And but one word with one of us? Couple it with something; make it a word and a blow.	
TYBALT.	You shall find me apt enough to that, sir, an you will give me occasion.	
MERCUTIO.	Could you not take some occasion without giving?	
TYBALT.	Mercutio, thou consort'st with Romeo, –	40
MERCUTIO.	Consort! What! dost thou make us minstrels? an thou make minstrels of us, look to hear nothing but discords: here's my fiddlestick; here's that shall make you dance. 'Zounds! consort!	
BENVOLIO.	We talk here in the public haunt of men: Either withdraw unto some private place, Or reason coldly of your grievances, Or else depart; here all eyes gaze on us.	
MERCUTIO.	Men's eyes were made to look, and let them gaze; I will not budge for no man's pleasure, I.	50

Enter ROMEO.

TYBALT.	Well, peace be with you, sir. Here comes my man.	
MERCUTIO.	But I'll be hang'd sir, if he wear your livery: Marry, go before to field, he'll be your follower; Your worship in that sense may call him 'man'.	
TYBALT.	Romeo, the hate I bear thee can afford No better term than this, – thou art a villain.	
ROMEO.	Tybalt, the reason that I have to love thee Doth much excuse the appertaining rage To such a greeting; villain am I none, Therefore farewell; I see thou know'st me not.	60
TYBALT.	Boy, this shall not excuse the injuries That thou has done me; therefore turn and draw.	
ROMEO.	I do protest I never injur'd thee, But love thee better than thou canst devise, Till thou shalt know the reason of my love: And so, good Capulet, which name I tender As dearly as my own, be satisfied.	
MERCUTIO.	O calm, dishonourable, vile submission! Alla stoccata carries it away. [*Draws.*	
	Tybalt, you rat-catcher, will you walk?	70
TYBALT.	What wouldst thou have with me?	
MERCUTIO.	Good king of cats, nothing but one of your nine lives, that I mean to make bold withal, and, as you shall use me hereafter, dry-beat the rest of the eight. Will you pluck your sword out of his pilcher by the ears? make haste, lest mine be about your ears ere it be out.	

TYBALT.	[Drawing.] I am for you.
ROMEO.	Gentle Mercutio, put thy rapier up.
MERCUTIO.	Come, sir, your passado. [They fight.
ROMEO.	Draw, Benvolio; beat down their weapons. 80
	Gentlemen, for shame, forbear this outrage!
	Tybalt, Mercutio, the prince expressly hath
	Forbidden bandying in Verona streets.
	Hold, Tybalt! good Mercutio!

[Exeunt TYBALT and his Partisans.

MERCUTIO.	I am hurt.
	A plague o'both your houses! I am sped.
	Is he gone, and hath nothing?
BENVOLIO.	What! art thou hurt?
MERCUTIO.	Ay, ay, a scratch, a scratch; marry, 'tis enough.
	Where is my page? Go, villain, fetch a surgeon. 90

[Exit Page.

ROMEO.	Courage, man; the hurt cannot be much.
MERCUTIO.	No, 'tis not so deep as a well, nor so wide as a church door; but 'tis enough, 'twill serve: ask for me to-morrow, and you shall find me a grave man. I am peppered, I warrant, for this world. A plague o' both your houses! 'Zounds, a dog, a rat, a mouse, a cat, to scratch a man to death! a braggart, a rogue, a villain, that fights by the book of arithmetic! Why the devil came you between us? I was hurt under your arm.
ROMEO.	I thought all for the best.
MERCUTIO.	Help me into some house, Benvolio, 100
	Or I shall faint. A plague o' both your houses!
	They have made worms' meat of me: I have it,
	And soundly too: – your houses!

[Exeunt MERCUTIO and BENVOLIO.

ROMEO.	This gentleman, the prince's near ally,
	My friend, hath got his mortal hurt
	In my behalf; my reputation stain'd
	With Tybalt's slander, Tybalt, that an hour
	Hath been my kinsman. O sweet Juliet!
	Thy beauty hath made me effeminate,
	And in my temper soften'd valour's steel! 110

Re-enter BENVOLIO.

BENVOLIO.	O Romeo, Romeo! brave Mercutio's dead;
	That gallant spirit hath aspir'd the clouds,
	Which too untimely here did scorn the earth.
ROMEO.	This day's black fate on more days doth depend;
	This but begins the woe others must end.

Re-enter TYBALT.

BENVOLIO.	Here comes the furious Tybalt back again.
ROMEO.	Alive! in triumph! and Mercutio slain!
	Away to heaven, respective lenity,
	And fire-ey'd fury be my conduct now!
	Now, Tybalt, take the villain back again 120

	That late thou gav'st me; for Mercutio's soul	
	Is but a little way above our heads,	
	Staying for thine to keep him company:	
	Either thou, or I, or both, must go with him.	
TYBALT.	Thou wretched boy, that didst consort him here,	
	Shalt with him hence.	
ROMEO.	This shall determine that.	

[They fight: TYBALT falls.

BENVOLIO.	Romeo, away! be gone!	
	The citizens are up, and Tybalt slain.	
	Stand not amaz'd: the prince will doom thee death	130
	If thou art taken: hence! be gone! away!	
ROMEO.	O! I am Fortune's fool.	
BENVOLIO.	Why dost thou stay?	

[Exit ROMEO

Enter Citizens, &c.

FIRST CITIZEN.	Which way ran he that kill'd Mercutio?	
	Tybalt, that murderer, which way ran he?	
BENVOLIO.	There lies that Tybalt.	
FIRST CITIZEN.	Up, sir, go with me.	
	I charge thee in the prince's name, obey.	

Enter PRINCE, attended; MONTAGUE, CAPULET, their Wives, and Others.

PRINCE.	Where are the vile beginners of this fray?	
BENVOLIO.	O noble prince! I can discover all	140
	The unlucky manage of this fatal brawl:	
	There lies the man, slain by young Romeo,	
	That slew thy kinsman, brave Mercutio.	
LADY CAPULET.	Tybalt, my cousin! O my brother's child!	
	O prince! O cousin! husband! O! the blood is spill'd	
	Of my dear kinsman. Prince, as thou art true,	
	For blood of ours shed blood of Montague.	
	O cousin, cousin!	
PRINCE.	Benvolio, who began this bloody fray?	
BENVOLIO.	Tybalt, here slain, whom Romeo's hand did slay:	150
	Romeo, that spoke him fair, bade him bethink	
	How nice the quarrel was, and urg'd withal	
	Your high displeasure: all this, uttered	
	With gentle breath, calm look, knees humbly bow'd,	
	Could not take truce with the unruly spleen	
	Of Tybalt deaf to peace, but that he tilts	
	With piercing steel at bold Mercutio's breast,	
	Who, all as hot, turns deadly point to point,	
	And, with a martial scorn, with one hand beats	
	Cold death aside, and with the other sends	160
	It back to Tybalt, whose dexterity	
	Retorts it: Romeo he cries aloud,	
	'Hold, friends! friends, part!' and, swifter than his tongue,	
	His agile arm beats down their fatal points,	
	And 'twixt them rushes; underneath whose arm	
	An envious thrust from Tybalt hit the life	

Of stout Mercutio, and then Tybalt fled;
But by and by comes back to Romeo,
Who had but newly entertain'd revenge,
And to 't they go like lightning, for, ere I   170
Could draw to part them, was stout Tybalt slain,
And, as he fell, did Romeo turn and fly.
This is the truth, or let Benvolio die.

LADY CAPULET. He is a kinsman to the Montague;
Affection makes him false, he speaks not true: 176
Some twenty of them fought in this black strife
And all those twenty could but kill one life.
I beg for justice, which thou, prince must give;
Romeo slew Tybalt, Romeo must not live.

PRINCE. Romeo slew him, he slew Mercutio;   180
Who now the price of his dear blood doth owe?

MONTAGUE. Not Romeo, prince, he was Mercutio's friend,
His fault concludes but what the law should end,   184
The life of Tybalt.

PRINCE. And for that offence
Immediately we do exile him hence:
I have an interest in your hate's proceeding,
My blood for your rude brawls doth lie a-bleeding;
But I'll amerce you with so strong a fine
That you shall all repent the loss of mine.   190
I will be deaf to pleading and excuses;
Nor tears nor prayers shall purchase out abuses;
Therefore use none; let Romeo hence in haste,
Else, when he's found, that hour is his last.
Bear hence this body and attend our will:
Mercy but murders, pardoning those that kill.   [Exeunt.

ENGLISH: PAPER 2 (ii)

ANSWERS: Understanding and response

Romeo and Juliet

There are 30 marks available for this section: 15 for Understanding and Response and 15 for Written Expression. The mark scheme below is for Understanding and Response, and incorporates the full 15 marks available. Please see page 40 for detailed comments on how to assess written expression.

After checking your child's answers against the mark scheme, decide where it best fits on to the following scale:

Mark 13 – 15:	*Exceptional performance*	(Above Level 7)
Mark 10 – 12:	*Well above average*	(Level 7)
Mark 8 – 9:	*Above average/average*	(Level 6)
Mark 6 – 7:	*Average/below average*	(Level 5)
Mark 3 – 5:	*Well below average*	(Level 4 or below)

The instructions allow pupils to answer this question in more than one way. Whichever approach is taken, the answer should point out, and illustrate by quotation, the following:

- **Mercutio's view of quarrelling and his conversation with Tybalt.**
  (a) He will quarrel to defend himself against personal insults (line 37).
  (b) He is hot-headed and excitable, almost looking for a fight before it happens.
  (c) If *honour* is at stake, he will not hesitate to enter a quarrel (line 52). (d) When he is roused, he cannot be prevented from quarrelling (lines 68–69). (e) His attitude to quarrelling is much more complex than that of Tybalt, whose sole purpose is to draw any Montague in sight into a fight because he enjoys acting like the thug that he is.

- **Mercutio's reasons for fighting with Tybalt.** (a) He fights to defend Romeo, first because they are friends and second because they are kinsmen; it is not mainly to assert himself against Tybalt's taunts (line 52). (b) He thinks that Romeo's 'dishonourable, vile submission' is untypically feeble and cowardly; ironically, he does not know Romeo's reason (i.e. Juliet) for wishing to make peace with the Capulets. (c) He shows his usual combination of rashness and courage.

- **Mercutio's attitude towards his own death.** (a) Typically, he makes light of his injuries even when he knows he is seriously hurt (line 89). (b) Although staring death in the face, he - again typically - takes pleasure in making jokes based on word-play ('... you shall find me a grave man'). (c) He is baffled by Romeo's intervention in the quarrel, which costs him his life (lines 97–98). (d) His last words express a sense of bitterness that he dies for the sake of an ancient grudge not of his own making ('A plague o'both your houses').

- **The scene's importance to the play.** Credit any point that *directly* links Mercutio's death with subsequent events. There are a great many of them! Pupils should show an appreciation that this is the scene on which everything that happens later in the play turns.

Written
expression

15

Marks for both
Understanding
and Response
and
Written
expression

TOTAL

When marking your child's Shakespeare answer out of 15 for Written Expression, use a 'best fit' procedure by (a) referring back to the assessment criteria listed on page 22 and (b) using the extract below from a candidate's answer in the 1996 test, which was awarded Level 5 (8 out of 15), and working 'up' or 'down' from it.

The audience seemed to enjoy our play, although I was a bit surprised at times, at how they responded to the prologue. I tried my best, so my grammar was a little muddled, there was no need to virtually jeer me off the stage. I think Theseus picked out too many bad points of my play, I think my actors did well and should be appraised we had few rehearsals and it was all rehearsed in the woods, so it wasn't easy to keep everyones mind on the job. I think if it wasn't for Bottom we would be lost, his enthusiasm kept us all going, he was ready to take on any part we threw at him his acting isn't quite up to scratch, but his good will couldn't be better, he kept us all smiling.
The play was written very carefully, I wanted to entertain. – make people laugh, cry and get involved in the play, I think I succeeded.
Because of the ladies preas present I had to be very careful not to scare them with the lion, so when snug

ENGLISH: ANSWERS

Conversion of score into National Curriculum levels

Having worked through both Paper 1 and Paper 2, it is now possible for your child's performance to be awarded a single overall Level. This is the procedure followed in the test itself: the marks for both papers are totalled (not aggregrated) and, in July, s/he receives a certificated grade for English at Key Stage 3.

Calculate the overall Level as follows:

1. Add together your child's marks for Paper 1 - a maximum of 18 for Section A, 10 for Section B, and 22 for Section C.
2. Add this to your child's total for Paper 2 (maximum 40) to produce an overall mark out of 90.
3. Read off the table below* to find your child's Level:

Mark	Level
80	7+
76	7
72	7–
70	6+
66	6
62	6–
60	5+
56	5
52	5–
50	4+
46	4
42	4–

*This table © Stanley Thornes 1997. It is not issued by either SCAA or DFEE.

MATHEMATICS

Testing your child's mathematics

What do the National Tests cover?

The National Curriculum at Key Stage 3 is divided into four areas called 'Attainment Targets'. The four attainment targets are:

1 Using and Applying Mathematics
2 Number and Algebra
3 Shape, Space and Measures
4 Handling Data

Using and Applying Mathematics consists of practical and investigational work involving the other three Attainment Targets. It does not form part of the National Tests but is assessed by the school. For the tests in May your child will probably sit three papers, two of these being ordinary written papers (one of which will be a non-calculator paper) and the third being a mental test. There will be four tiers of entry at National Curriculum levels 3–5, 4–6, 5–7 and 6–8.

What do these practice papers cover?

For ease of use and also to give a student maximum practice, this book contains two tests. These cover the most popular tiers of entry at levels 4–6 and 5–7. Each paper contains 15 questions, five questions at each of the levels covered. For example Paper 1 has questions 1–5 at level 4, 6–10 at level 5 and 11–15 at level 6. Some of the questions are marked 'no calculator'. These are most likely to be on a separate 'no calculator' paper in the National Tests. Here the problems have been kept together to help you get a better idea of your child's level. There is also a third paper which is made up of mental questions.

Setting the tests (time: 1 hour each test)

1 Paper 1 should be done first. If this is successfully completed then Paper 2 may be attempted. It is important to remember that an average student may not have studied all the topics included in these tests.

2 Your child will need:
- a pencil and a ruler
- a calculator; preferably a scientific calculator but there should be a $\sqrt{}$ key.
- a protractor
- tracing paper

3 As with all tests a student who finishes early should check the work thoroughly.

Mental work at Key Stage 3

1 Check that your child knows his or her tables up to 10×10 as thoroughly as possible.

2 Get your child to practise adding and subtracting mentally, e.g. $18 + 7$ or $36 - 12$ Help them with strategies like $80 - 48$ is $80 - 50$ then take away 2.

3 At Level 5 a student should be able to multiply or divide a number, including a decimal, by 10, 100 or 1000, e.g. $34 \div 10$ or 7.5×100.

4 At Level 4 a student should be able to check calculations from the context or the size of the numbers.

5 At level 7 a student should be able to check calculations by rounding to one significant figure, e.g. $3145 \div 5.7$ is about 3000 divided by 6 which is 500.

Written non-calculator work at Key Stage 3

1 At Level 4 a student should be able to add and subtract decimals and do short multiplication and division by whole numbers, e.g. set out properly and work out $3.6 + 15.2$ or 5.04×7.

2 At Level 5 a student should be able to do long multiplication or long division by whole two-digit numbers, e.g. set out properly and work out 6.82×27 or $598 \div 23$.

Formulae

You might need to use these formulae.

AREA

Circle

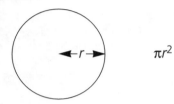

πr^2

Rectangle

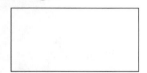

length × width

Triangle

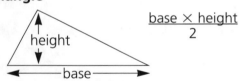

$\dfrac{\text{base} \times \text{height}}{2}$

Parallelogram

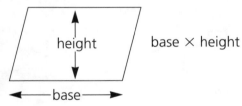

base × height

Trapezium

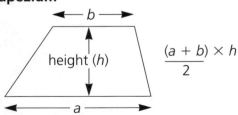

$\dfrac{(a + b) \times h}{2}$

LENGTH

Circle

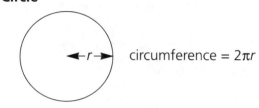

circumference = $2\pi r$

For a right-angled triangle

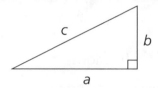

$a^2 + b^2 = c^2$ (Pythagoras' theorem)

VOLUME

Prism

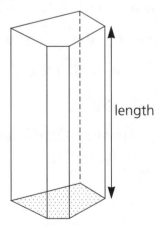

area of cross-section × length

MATHEMATICS: Mental Paper

Test

1 Multiply 6 by 8

2 Take 29 away from 54

3 What is 23 multiplied by 100?

4 What is 500 divided by 10?

5 What fraction is the same as 50%?

6 Multiply 0.9 by 1000

7 Divide 45 by 10

8 What is 10% of 200?

9 What is $\frac{3}{4}$ of 36?

10 Multiply 20 by 60

11 What is 0.7 as a fraction?

12 What percentage is 5 of 20?

13 What is $\frac{3}{4}$ as a decimal number?

14 What is 20% as a fraction?
Give your answer as simply as possible.

15 Give 13.89 correct to the nearest whole number.

16 Estimate the answer to 529×6.7

17 Divide 15 by 0.5

18 Estimate the answer to 3928 divided by 18

19 Multiply 0.01 by 2

20 What is 0.7 multiplied by 0.8?

MATHEMATICS: Mental Paper

Answers

1 48

2 $54 - 29 = 54 - 9 - 20$
$= 45 - 20$
$= 25$

3 2300

4 50

5 $\frac{1}{2}$

6 900 There are 3 noughts in 1000 so the 9 moves across 3 columns.

0.9

↙

9 0 0.

7 4.5

8 $10\% \text{ of } 200 = \frac{1}{10} \text{ of } 200$
$= 20$

9 $\frac{1}{4}$ of $36 = 9$
$\frac{3}{4}$ of $36 = 3 \times 9$
$= 27$

10 1200

11 The 7 is in the tenths column so $0.7 = \frac{7}{10}$

12 5 is $\frac{1}{4}$ of 20; $\frac{1}{4} = 25\%$

13 $\frac{3}{4} = 3 \div 4 = 0.75$

14 $\frac{20}{100} = \frac{1}{5}$

15 14

16 $500 \times 7 = 3500$

17 30 When dividing by a number less than 1, the answer is larger.

18 $4000 \div 20 = 200$

19 0.02

20 0.56

1 **Dotty patterns**

Liz puts **1 small triangular tile** on triangular dotty paper like this.

Ben makes a bigger triangle with **4 small triangular tiles** like this.

Ravi makes a bigger triangle with **9 small triangular tiles** like this.

 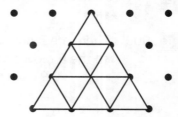

(a) Draw a bigger triangle on the dotty paper. **Use 16 tiles**.

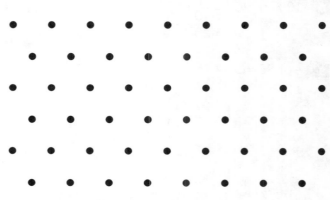

The triangles have these numbers of tiles: **1**, **4**, **9**, **16**

Liz has found **a pattern** that makes these numbers.

Here is Liz's pattern:

$$1 = \mathbf{1}$$
$$1 + 3 = \mathbf{4}$$
$$1 + 3 + 5 = \mathbf{9}$$

(b) Fill in the **next two lines** in Liz's pattern

.... = **16**

.... = ...

2 Symmetry

Paul shades in a shape made of five squares on a grid.

He shades **1 more square** to make a shape which has the dashed line as a **line of symmetry**.

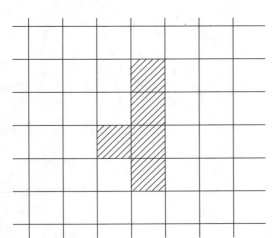 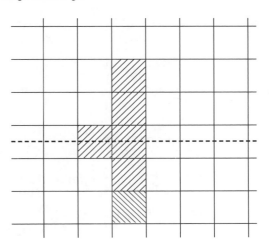

(a) Shade in **1 more square** in each of these to make a new shape. The dashed line needs to be a **line of symmetry** in each new shape. You can use a mirror or tracing paper to help you.

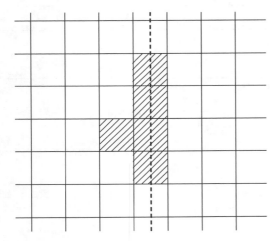

(b) Shade in **2 more squares** to make a shape with the dashed line as a **line of symmetry**.

You can use a mirror or tracing paper to help you.

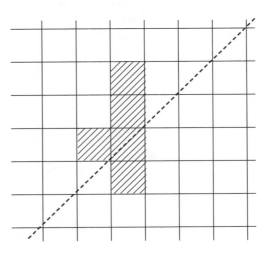

2

1

3 Flags

Carl is making coloured flags.

(a) About 50% of this flag is red.

Fill in each gap with a **percentage**.

About ...... % is blue.

About ...... % is white.

RED	BLUE
	WHITE

2

(b) About $\frac{1}{6}$ of this flag is black.

Fill in each gap with a **fraction**.

About ...... of this flag is yellow.

About ...... of this flag is green.

BLACK
YELLOW
GREEN

2

(c) About $\frac{3}{5}$ of this flag is orange.

Draw a straight line to show how much of the flag is orange.

Shade in the area that is orange.

2

TOTAL

4 Traffic

Jean did a traffic survey outside her school.
She recorded the **number of people** who were **in each car**.
This table shows her data for two times of the day.
Jean surveyed 30 cars for each of the two times.

8.15 am to 9.00 am						9.00 am to 9.45 am				
2	3	4	1	3		1	1	1	2	1
2	3	2	1	1		1	3	2	1	1
3	2	3	2	3		3	1	2	1	3
1	2	1	2	2		2	2	1	3	1
3	1	2	4	2		1	1	2	1	1
2	3	3	2	3		2	3	1	1	1

Jean made a tally chart of the people in the cars.

Number of people in each car	Time		Total number of people for both times
	8.15 am to 9.00 am	9.00 am to 9.45 am	
1	卌 I		
2	卌 卌 II		
3	卌 卌		
4	II		2

(a) **Tally** the number of people in the cars for **9.00 am to 9.45 am**.
Then fill in the column for the **total number of people for both times**.

(b) Jean says:

24 is the **mode** of the numbers of people in the cars.

Is Jean right?
Explain your answer.

....

....

(c) How did the **number of people** in the cars **change** between the two times?
Suggest a reason for this change in the number of people.

....

TOTAL

5 Co-ordinates

Colin joins four points on a grid to make a shape.

The **co-ordinates** are:
(0, 0), (3, 0), (2, 1), (1, 1)
The **area** of Colin's shape is 2 cm²

Colin's shape

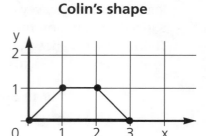

Jenni **multiplies** each of Colin's co-ordinates **by 2**.

Jenni's shape

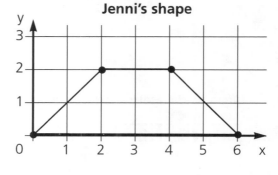

Colin's co-ordinates	× 2	Jenni's co-ordinates
(0, 0)	→	**(0, 0)**
(3, 0)	→	**(6, 0)**
(2, 1)	→	**(4, 2)**
(1, 1)	→	**(2, 2)**

(a) What is the **area** of Jenni's shape?

Area = ... cm²

(b) **Multiply** each of Colin's co-ordinates **by 3**.

Colin's co-ordinates	× 3	New co-ordinates
(0, 0)	→	(........., ...)
(3, 0)	→	(........., ...)
(2, 1)	→	(........., ...)
(1, 1)	→	(........., ...)

Plot the 4 points with the new co-ordinates on the grid.
Join the points to make a shape.

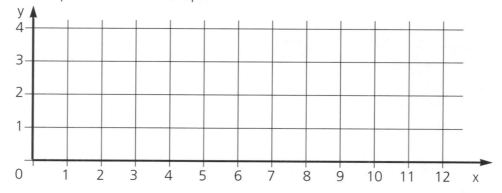

(c) What is the area of your shape?   Area = ... cm²

6 **Number cards**

Rob has these number cards:

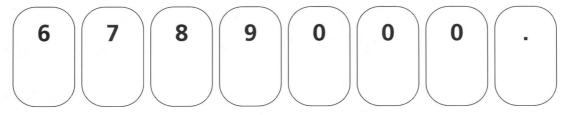

| 6 | 7 | 8 | 9 | 0 | 0 | 0 | . |

Rob chose two cards:

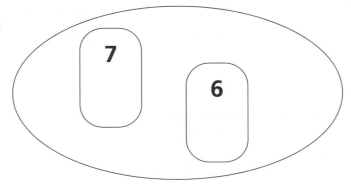

7

6

He made the number **67** with his two cards.

(a) Rob then made a number **1000 times** as big as **67**.
Show the number that Rob made.

1

(b) Rob made the number **69.8** with his cards.

Rob then made a number that was **10 times** as big as **69.8**.
Show the number that Rob made.

1

Rob then used the cards to make a number **100 times** bigger than **69.8**.
Show the number that Rob made.

1

TOTAL

7 **Tile patterns**

Bev is making a series of patterns with triangular and square tiles.

Pattern
number 1

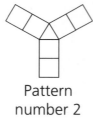

Pattern
number 2

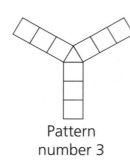

Pattern
number 3

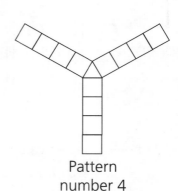

Pattern
number 4

Each pattern has **1 triangular tile** at the centre.
Each new pattern has **more square tiles** than the one before.

(a) How many more square tiles does Bev add each time she makes a new pattern?

.... square tiles

(b) Bev says:

The rule for finding
the total number of tiles in
pattern number **n** is :
**total number of tiles
= 3 × n + 1**

The **1** in Bev's rule is for the triangular tile.
What does the **3 × n** represent?

....

(c) Bev wants to make **pattern number 12**.
How many **triangular** and how many **square** tiles does she need?

.... triangular and .... square tiles

(d) Bev uses **61 tiles** altogether to make a pattern.
What is the number of the pattern that she makes?

pattern number ....

(e) Bev has **13 triangular** tiles and **90 square** tiles.
What is the number of the **biggest** pattern that Bev can make?

pattern number ....

TOTAL

8 **Angles**

You need a ruler and a protractor or an angle measurer for this question.

Den has drawn this **triangle**.

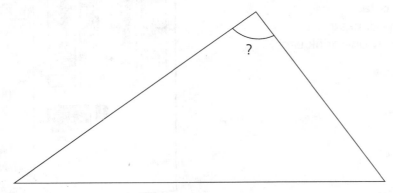

(a) **Measure** the **top angle** of Den's triangle. ....°

1

(b) Katie wants to draw this triangle.
She has drawn a line AB.
Katie wants an angle of **28° at A**.
She wants an angle of **123° at B**.

Finish Katie's triangle.

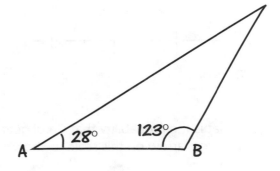

A _____ B

2

TOTAL

9 Drinks

This drinks machine is broken.
You **cannot choose** the drink you get!

Brian **only likes cola**.
Carol **likes all** the drinks.
Carol and Brian buy one drink each.

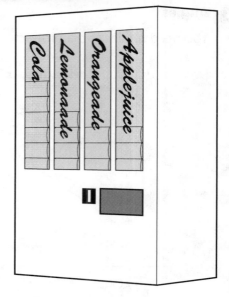

(a) What is the probability that Brian gets a drink he likes?
Draw an arrow on this scale to show the probability that Brian gets a drink he likes.

0   1

(b) What is the probability that Carol gets a drink she likes?
Draw an arrow on this scale to show the probability that Carol gets a drink that she likes.

0   1

(c) Jane buys one drink.
The arrow shows the probability that Jane gets a drink that she likes.

Jane

0   1

Write a sentence about the drinks that Jane likes.

....

....

TOTAL

10 **Shampoo**

This **standard size** bottle of hair shampoo contains **150 ml**.

(a) How much shampoo is in this **special offer** bottle which is **20% bigger**?

.... ml

2

(b) Jill can wash her hair **10 times** with the **standard size**.

How many times can she wash her hair with the **special offer size**?

....

1

(c) Jill's hairdresser uses an **extra large** bottle of the shampoo containing **1.8 litres**.

How many **millilitres** of shampoo does the **extra large** size contain?

.... ml

1

TOTAL

11 Poetry reading

Don, Ann and Jo are in a poetry reading competition.

To decide the order in which they will read all three names are put into a box. Each name is taken out, one at a time, without looking.

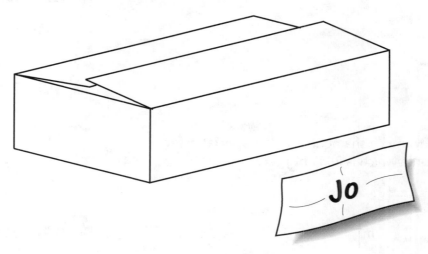

(a) Write down **all the possible orders** for the names.

(b) Write down the **probability** that Jo reads **first**.

(c) Jo enters a different competition with 6 readers.

The **probability** that Jo will read **first** is $\frac{1}{6}$.

Write down the **probability** that Jo will **not** read **first**.

2

1

1

TOTAL

12 **Straight lines**

The diagram shows the graph of the straight line **y = 2x**.

(a) Draw the straight line **y = 3x**.
Label your line **y = 3x**.

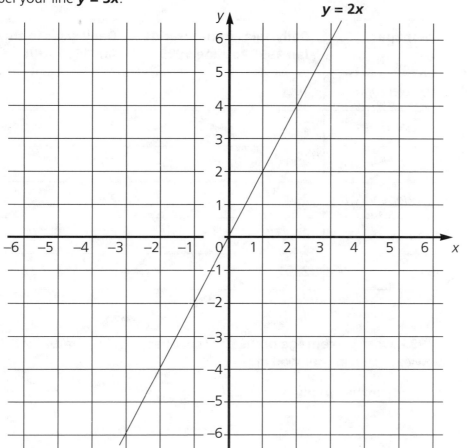

1

(b) Write the equation of another straight line which goes through the point **(0, 0)**.

....

1

(c) The straight line **y = x – 2** goes through the point **(5, 3)**.
Draw the graph of **y = x – 2** on the diagram.
Label the line **y = x – 2**.

1

(d) Write the equation of the straight line which is parallel to **y = 2x** and which goes through the point **(0, –2)**.

y = ...

1

TOTAL

13 **Newspapers**

Sian is doing an investigation into **daily newspapers**. She is using this table.
The table shows the **average daily sales** of each of the broadsheet newspapers in
the first half of the year for **1995** and **1996**.

Newspaper	Daily sales in thousands Jan 1995 to June 1995	Daily sales in thousands Jan 1996 to June 1996
Daily Telegraph	1066	1044
Financial Times	294	302
The Guardian	400	398
The Independent	294	279
The Times	647	685
Total	2301	2708

(a) In **1995**, what **percentage** of the daily newspapers sold were **Daily Telegraphs**?
Show each step in your working.

....

....

............%

2

(b) In **1996**, for every copy of **The Independent** that was sold, how many **Daily Telegraphs** were sold?
Show your working.

....

....

.... **Daily Telegraphs**

1

(c) Calculate the percentage increase in the sales of **The Times** from **1995 to 1996**.
Show your working.

....

....

.... %

2

TOTAL

14 **Computer commands**

Megan is making patterns on a computer.
She has only two commands for her patterns.

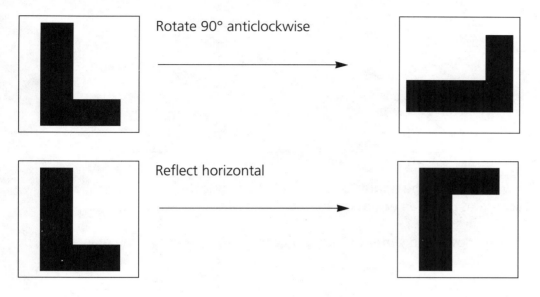

Rotate 90° anticlockwise

Reflect horizontal

Complete the instructions for these.

(a)

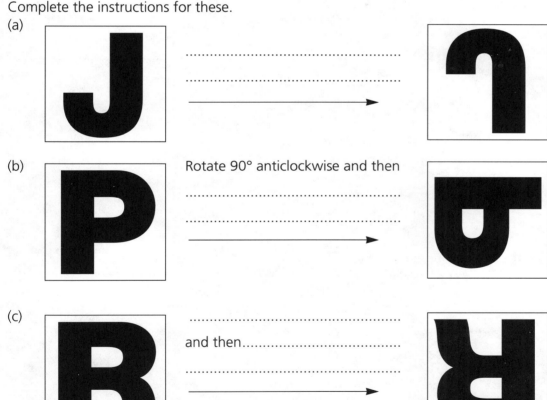

....
....

 1

(b) Rotate 90° anticlockwise and then
....
....

 1

(c) ....
and then...................................
....

 2

TOTAL

15 **Triangle**

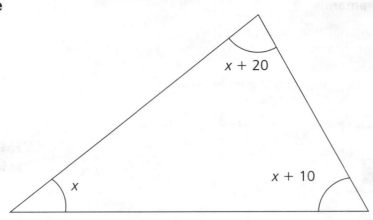

Tracy knows that the **angles of a triangle** add up to **180°**.
Tracy writes down an **equation** for the angles of this triangle.

(a) Write down and **simplify** Tracy's equation for the angles of the triangle.

....
....
....
....
....
....
....
....
....

(b) **Solve** your equation to find x.
Show your working.

....
....
....
....
....
....
....
....

$x = $ ......

1

2

TOTAL

1 Marbles

Vali, Sharon, Jon and Mandy each start a game with one or more boxes of marbles. There are **m marbles in each box**.

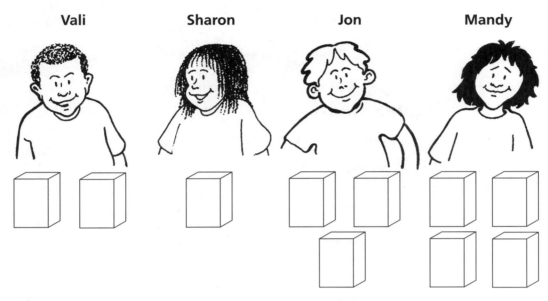

| | Vali | Sharon | Jon | Mandy |

The table shows what happens during the game.

(a) Write expressions to show the number of marbles that Jon and Mandy have at the end of the game.
Write each expression **as simply as possible**.

	Start	During game	End of game
Vali	2 boxes	lost 7 marbles	2 m − 7
Sharon	1 box	won 5 marbles	m + 5
Jon	3 boxes	won 6 marbles	
Mandy	4 boxes	lost 8 marble and won 4 marbles	

3

(b) The number of marbles m in a box is **12**.
How many marbles does Vali have at the **end of the game**?

.... marbles

1

TOTAL

2 **Pea soup**

Ken has an old recipe for pea soup.

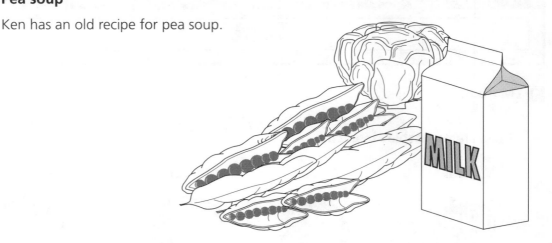

Pea soup

2 pounds of peas in their pods.

Six lettuce leaves

1 $\frac{3}{4}$ pints of milk

water

Shell the peas. Boil the pods in a little water for 30 minutes.

Use this water to cook the peas and lettuce until soft.

Sieve the peas and lettuce and add the milk.

Serve hot or cold.

Ken needs to change the amounts to **metric** measures.

Fill in the gaps to show the **approximate amounts** and the **units** which Ken should use.

Pea soup

About .... of peas in their pods.

Six lettuce leaves

About .... of milk

water

2

2

TOTAL

3 **Pie charts**

There are **36 pupils** in Sian's class.
Sian has done a survey of the favourite subject of each person in the class.

Here are Sian's results.

Subject	Number of people
Art	11
Maths	7
PE	9
English	6
Science	3

She has started this pie chart to show the results.

Sian's class (36 pupils)

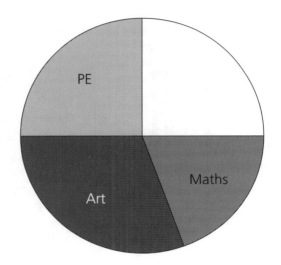

(a) 6 people chose **English**.
Show this on Sian's pie chart as accurately as you can.
Label this part **English**.
Label the remaining part **science**.

2

(b) There are **24 pupils** in Lewis's class.
Lewis has done the same survey.
He has also drawn a pie chart.
2 people chose **science** and 9 people chose **PE**.
On Lewis's pie chart write how many pupils chose **maths**, **English** and **art**.

Lewis's class (24 pupils)

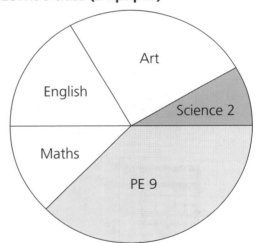

2

Lewis says,

"There are **9 people** in my class who chose **PE**. There are **9 people** in Sian's class who chose PE. Sian's pie chart shows **PE** as a **smaller part** than mine. Sian must be wrong."

(c) Explain why Lewis is wrong.

1

TOTAL

4 **Purses**

Lil makes purses to sell.
She sells the purses for **£2.65** each.

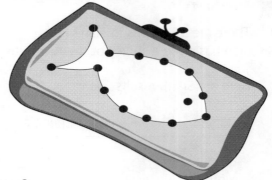

(a) Lil sells **27** purses.
How much does she get for the **27** purses?

Remember to write down enough working to show you have not used a calculator.

Working:

....

....

....

....

....

£ ....

(b) Lil has a box of 300 beads.
She uses 14 beads to make the fish pattern on each purse.
How many complete purses can she make using the 300 beads?

Remember to write down enough working to show you have not used a calculator.

Working:

....

....

....

....

....

.... purses

2

2

TOTAL

5 **Tiles**

This is a square tile.

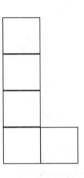

The edge of the tile is **t** centimetres.
The **perimeter** of the tile is **4t centimetres**.

This **L-shape** is made with **5 square tiles**.

(a) Write an **expression** for the **perimeter**
of the **L-shape**.

The expression should be a **number
multiplied by t**.

....

(b) The perimeter of the shape is **24** centimetres.
Use your expression from part (a) to write an **equation** involving **t**.

....

....

....

....

....

....

....

....

Solve your equation to find the **value** of **t**.

....

....

....

....

....

....

....

t = ...

6 **Cafe**

Mary and Bill work in a cafe.

Mary thinks there is a **relationship** between the **number of cups of tea sold** and **the number of burgers sold**.
Mary recorded the number of cups of tea sold and the number of burgers sold for 12 days.
Mary drew this graph to test her ideas.

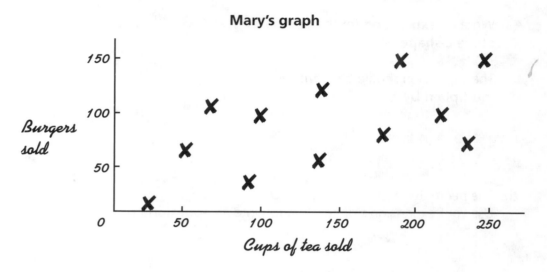

Bill thinks there is a **relationship** between **the number of cold drinks sold** and **how hot the weather is**.
Bill recorded the number of cold drinks sold and how hot the day was for 12 days.
Bill drew this graph to test his ideas.

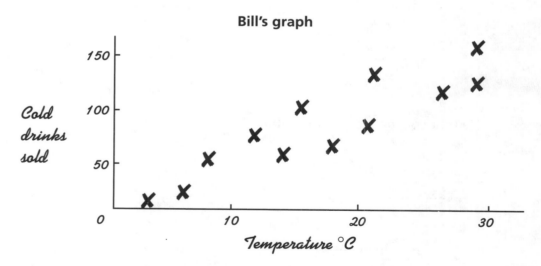

(a) Whose graph shows a **strong relationship**?

.... 's graph

(b) Explain why the other graph shows a **relationship** which is **less strong**.

....

7 Cubes

Val has drawn this **net** of a **cube**.

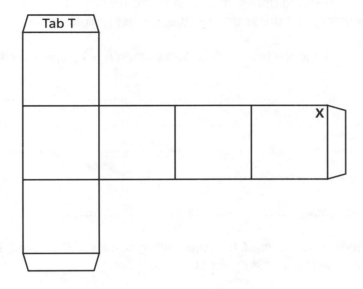

Val folds up the net.

(a) Write **T** on the edge that **tab T** will be stuck to.

(b) One of the corners is marked **X**.
Write **X** in **each of the other two corners** that will **meet** the corner marked **X**.

Steve has a different net of a cube.
He is marking the faces with spots to make a **die**.
Opposite faces have to **add up to 7**.

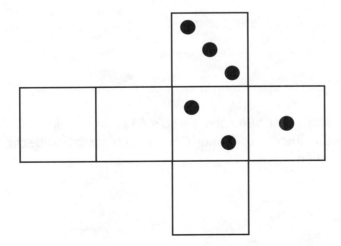

(c) Finish marking the spots on the die.

8 **Drinks**

Don's snack bar sells hot drinks for 60p and cold drinks for 40p.
The money from selling drinks, **d**, can be found from the formula **d = 60h + 40c**.
h is the number of hot drinks and **c** is the number of cold drinks.

(a) Work out the money from selling drinks when **h = 25** and **c = 41**.

....

....

....

....

£ ....

(b) One Saturday Don made **£49 from selling drinks**. If **Don sold 35 hot drinks**
that day, how many cold drinks did he sell?

....

....

....

....

cold drinks ....

(c) On hot days Don expects the **ratio of hot drinks to cold drinks** to be about **2:3**.
How many cold drinks does Don expect to sell on a hot day when he sells 40
drinks?

....

....

....

....

cold drinks ....

(d) Don sells biscuits for **18p** each. He sold **4123** biscuits in April.
Estimate the amount of money Don made from selling biscuits in April.
Show your working.

....

....

....

....

£ ....

9 **Jogging**

200 pupils from Years 7–11 at Ardern High School took part in a sponsored jog.
Terry drew this graph.

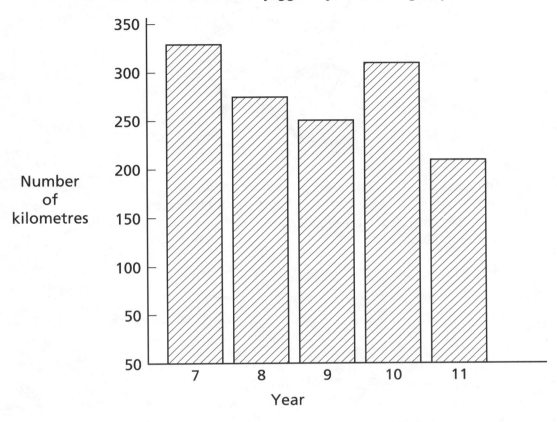

Number of kilometres jogged by each Year group

Use your graph to answer these questions.

(a) Did Year 9 have **more** pupils taking part in the jog than Year 8?
Tick the correct box.

Yes ☐   No ☐   Cannot tell ☐

Explain your answer.

....

....

....

1

(b) Use the graph to work out the **mean** number of kilometres jogged by each of
the 200 pupils.

....

....

....

2

TOTAL

10

Bicycles

(a) The wheels on Tod's bike have a **diameter** of **65 cm**.
Tod pushes the bike so that the wheels go round **exactly** once.
Calculate how far the bike has moved.
Show your working.

....

....

....

....

.... cm

2

(b) Gemma pushes her bike so that the wheels go round exactly once.
The bike moves forward 220 cm.
Calculate the diameter of one of the wheels on Gemma's bike.

....

....

....

....

.... cm

2

TOTAL

11 **Sports shop**

A sports shop had a sale.
For each day of the sale, prices were reduced by **15%** of the prices on the day before.

Danny bought these trainers on Saturday, the **second day** of the sale.

The **original price** of the trainers was **£49.95**.
How much did Danny pay for the trainers?

....
....
....
....
....
....
....

£ ....

2

TOTAL

12 **Finding numbers**

(a) Jim thought of two numbers which he called **p** and **q**.
He wrote down these equations for his numbers.

$$p + 2q = 17$$
$$4p + q = 26$$

Work out the values of **p** and **q**.
Show your working.

....

....

....

....

p = ... **q** = ...

(b) Harriet writes down an equation about the **area** of this rectangle.
The sides of her rectangle are **x** and **10 − x**.
Harriet wants to find the value of x which gives an area of **20** cm².

10 − x

x | Area 20 cm²

This is Harriet's equation.

$$x(10 - x) = 20$$

Between which **one decimal place** numbers does **x** lie?
You may use this table to work out your answer.

x	10 − x	area
4	6	24

between .... and ....

3

3

TOTAL

13 **Earth bank**

This bank of earth is in the shape of a **prism**. It is part of a new road works.

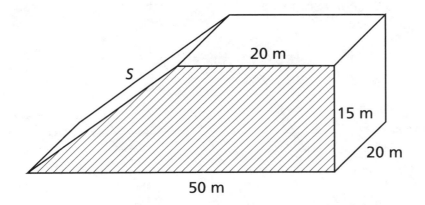

(a) The **shaded face** is to be covered with concrete.
Find the **area** of the shaded face.
Show your working.

....

....

....

....

.... m²

○
2

(b) Calculate the **total volume** of earth in the bank.
Show your working.

....

....

....

....

.... m³

○
1

(c) Calculate the **length** of the sloping edge, **s**.
Give your answer correct to 1 decimal place.
Show your working.

....

....

....

....

.... m

○
2

TOTAL

14 **Straws**

Pat is doing an experiment.
She drops **30** drinking straws at random on to the tiled floor.
She records the number of straws that fall so that they **are completely inside** a tile, not crossing a crack.

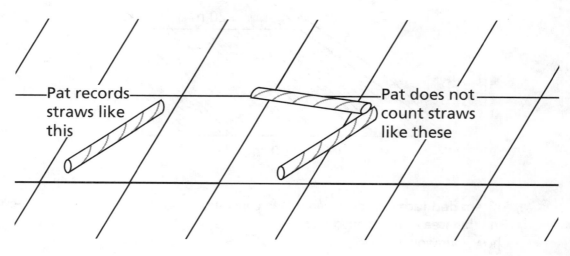

Pat drops the 30 straws **10 times**.
Here are her results.

9	8	12	6	10	12	7	8	15	6

(a) Use Pat's data to estimate the **probability** that **one straw** when dropped will fall so that it is **completely inside** a tile.

....
....
....
....
....

(b) Pat continues the experiment until she has dropped the 30 straws **50 times**.
About **how many straws in total** would you expect to be **completely inside** tiles?

....
....
....
....
....

2

2

TOTAL

15 **Formulas**

Terry is doing some work with formulas and triangles.

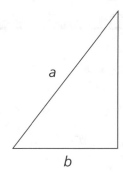

$c = \sqrt{a^2 - b^2}$

(a) Terry wants to find the length of side c of the triangle when $a = 12.5$ and $b = 7.5$
Terry puts the value of a and b into the formula.

$c = \sqrt{12.5^2 - 7.5^2}$

Work out the value of c.

....

....

....

....

....

....

1

(b) A formula for the area of the triangle is area $= \frac{1}{2}b\sqrt{a^2 - b^2}$

Terry wants to work out the area of the triangle when $a = 9.1$ and $b = 8.4$
Terry puts the new numbers into the formula.

area $= \frac{1}{2} \times 8.4 \times \sqrt{9.1^2 - 8.4^2}$

Work out the value of the area.

....

....

....

....

....

....

2

TOTAL

Paper 1

1 (a)   *1 mark*

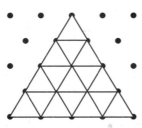

(b) 1 + 3 + 5 + 7 = 16
1 + 3 + 5 + 7 + 9 = 25   *2 marks*

2 (a)   *2 marks*   **(b)**   *1 mark*

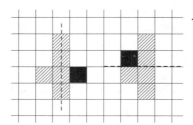   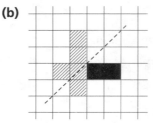

Hint
Practise using tracing paper and a mirror. With a mirror, the reflection and your drawing behind the mirror should look the same. If you use tracing paper, turn the paper over to get the reflection.

3 (a) About 20% is blue.
About 30% is white.   *2 marks*

Hint
25% is a quarter. The blue is a bit less than this and the white is a bit more.

(b) About $\frac{1}{3}$ is yellow. (Black is $\frac{1}{6}$. Yellow is twice as much and $\frac{2}{6} = \frac{1}{3}$)
About $\frac{1}{2}$ is green. (Green = 3 × black.)   *2 marks*

(c) Flag divided into five equal sections horizontally or vertically.and
three sections are shaded OR no lines but correct amount shaded.

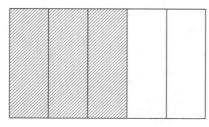   or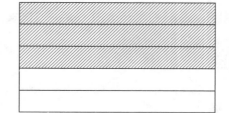

2 marks

4 (a)
1	⊪⊪⊪ ⊪⊪⊪ ⊪⊪⊪ ⦀	24
2	⊪⊪⊪ ⊪	19
3	⊪⊪⊪	15
4		2
		60

3 marks

(b) Jean is wrong. The mode is 1 person in a car.

Hint

This is a common mistake. The mode is **the situation** that occurs most frequently, not 24 which is just the largest frequency.

1 mark

(c) Before 9.00 am there were usually more people in each car.
Just before school nearly all the cars arriving would be dropping off pupils and so would contain more than one person.

1 mark

5 (a) 8 cm² *1 mark*

(b) (0, 0) → (0, 0)
(3, 0) → (9, 0)
(2, 1) → (6, 3)
(1, 1) → (3, 3)

There are no marks for the multiplication. The mark is for plotting the student's own co-ordinates correctly. If the multiplication is correct the shape looks like the diagram.

1 mark

(c) 18 cm² *1 mark*

6 (a) 67000 **(b)** 698 **(c)** 6980 *3 mark*

Hint

When multiplying decimals by 10, 100 etc, do not just add 0s.
Move the required number of figures past the decimal point.

$$\begin{array}{cc} 6\,9\,.\,8 \\ \times\,10 \end{array} \qquad \begin{array}{cc} 6\,9\,.\,8 \\ \times\,100 \end{array}$$

$$6\,9\,8\,.\,0 \qquad\qquad 6\,9\,8\,0\,.\,0$$

7 (a) 3 *1 mark*

(b) 3 × the number of square tiles in one 'branch'. *1 mark*

(c) 1 triangular tile and 3 × 12 = 36 square tiles. *1 mark*

(d) 3 × 20 + 1 = 61 so the pattern is number 20. *1 mark*

(e) Pattern number 30 (90 square tiles ÷ 3 = 30). *1 mark*

8 (a) 90° *1 mark*

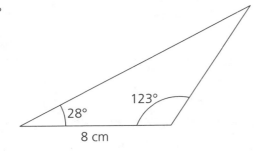

2 marks

Hint

Be careful of the two scales on the protractor. 28° is a small angle and 123° is more than 90°.

9 (a) The probability that Brian gets a drink he likes is $\frac{1}{4}$. (Brian likes one drink out of four.)

2 marks

TOTAL

(b) (Carol likes four drinks out of 4, $\frac{4}{4} = 1$)

0   1   *2 marks*

(c) The arrow for Jane is $\frac{3}{4}$ of the way along the line. This means Jane likes three out of four drinks.   *1 mark*

10 (a) 20% of 150 ml = 30 ml

The special offer bottle contains 150 ml + 30 ml = 180 ml   *2 marks*

(b) 20% of 10 times = 2 times

The special offer bottle will do 10 + 2 = 12 times.   *1 mark*

(c) 1.8 litres = 1.8 × 1000 = 1800 ml   *1 mark*

11 (a) Don   Ann   Jo

Don   Jo   Ann

Ann   Don   Jo

Ann   Jo   Don

Jo   Don   Ann

Jo   Ann   Don   *2 marks*

Hint
Work systematically. Write down all the answers with Don first, then with Ann first, etc.

(b) Jo reads first in two of the six possible arrangements.

The probability Jo reads first is $\frac{2}{6} = \frac{1}{3}$.   *1 mark*

(c) The probability that Jo will not read first is $1 - \frac{1}{6} = \frac{5}{6}$ *1 mark*

12 (a)

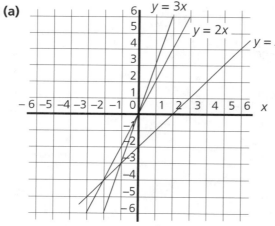

                                                                                                   1 mark

Hint
To draw a line, make up a small table. Two points will do, three are better.

X	0	1	2
y	0	3	6

(b) $y = x$, $y = 4x$, etc.   *1 mark*

(c) $y = 2 - x$ *1 mark*

(d) $y = 2x - 2$ *1 mark*

Hint
The number in front of x is the gradient. A line that is parallel needs the same gradient. The number added or subtracted is where the line cuts the y axis, in this case at −2.

13 (a) $\frac{1066}{2701} \times 100 = 39.5\%$ correct to 1 decimal place.   *2 marks*

  (b) $1044 \div 279 = 3.7$ correct to 1 decimal place.   *1 mark*

  (c) Increase in number of Times sold = 685 − 647 = 38

     % increase $= \frac{38}{647} \times 100 = 5.9\%$ correct to 1 decimal place.   *2 marks*

Hint

Where a calculator gives lots of figures, round off to something sensible.
In part c, write down the fractional increase before converting to a percentage.

14 (a) Reflect horizontal   *1 mark*

  (b) … reflect horizontal   *1 mark*

  (c) Rotate 90° anticlockwise and then rotate 90° anticlockwise.   *2 marks*

15 (a) $x + x + 20 + x + 10 = 3x + 30$
      $3x + 30 = 180$ *1 mark*

  (b) $3x + 30 - 30 = 180 - 30$
            $3x = 150$
              $x = 50$ *2 marks*

TOTAL

Paper 2

1 (a) Jon $3m + 6$
     Mandy $4m - 8 + 4 = 4m - 4$ *3 marks*

  (b) $2 \times 12 - 7 = 17$ *1 mark*

2 About **1 kilogram** of peas in their pods   *2 marks*
About **1 litre** of milk   *2 marks*

3 (a) There are 36 people altogether.
     Each person is represented by 360° ÷ 36 = 10°.
     The 6 people who chose English need 60°.   *2 marks*

  (b) **Method 1** 360° ÷ 24 = 15° or measure the science slice and divide by 2.
     Measure the angles for maths, English and art and divide each one by 15°.

     Method 2 Art is a quarter of the pie so 6 people chose art.
     English + art + science = half the pie = 12 people
     Maths + PE = half the pie = 12

     3 people chose Maths, 4 English and 6 Art   *2 marks*

  (c) Pie charts show proportion.
     In Sian's pie chart, PE is a quarter because 9 is a quarter of 36.
     In Lewis's pie chart, 9 is shown as a larger proportion of the whole pie of 24 people. *1 mark*

4 (a)
```
    2 . 6 5
  ×   2 7
  1 8  5 5
  5 3  0 0
      4 3
  1 1
 £ 7 1 . 5 5
   1
```
    2 marks

(b)
```
         2 1 rem 6
  14 ) 3 0 0
       2 8
       2 0
       1 4
        6
```

21 purses and 6 beads left over.   *2 marks*

5 (a) $12t$ *1 mark*   **(b)** $12t = 24$ *1 mark* $t = 12$ *1 mark*

6 (a) Bill's graph. *1 mark*   **(b)** The points in Mary's graph are in a broad band.   *1 mark*

Hint
This type of graph is called a scatter diagram. If points are randomly spread then there is no relationship. If points lie in a band, then there is a relationship. The closer the points are to a straight line, the stronger the relationship.

7 (a)

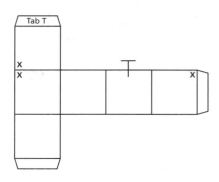

(b)

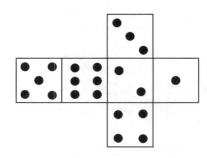

3 marks

2 marks

8 (a) £31.40

1 mark

(b) 35 hot drinks sell for 35 × 60 = £21
cold drinks sell for £49 − £21 = £28
number of cold drinks 2800 ÷ 40 = 70

2 marks

(c) 2 : 3 = 40 : 60 so there are 60 cold drinks.

1 mark

(d) 4123 × 18 ≈ 4000 × 20 = 80 000 = £800

2 marks

Hint
When you are asked to estimate, it means a rough calculation that you could work out in your head.

8 (a) ☑ Cannot tell   There could be lots of pupils doing short distances or fewer pupils going further.

1 mark

(b) $\dfrac{330 + 270 + 250 + 310 + 210}{200} = \dfrac{1370}{200} = 6.85$ km

2 marks

Hint
In this type of question, always ask yourself if the answer is sensible.
This helps to eliminate silly mistakes like dividing by 5 because there are 5 year groups.
$\dfrac{1370}{5} = 274$ km which is far too far for the pupils to jog.

10 (a) The bicycle will have moved by one circumference of the wheel.
C = πd or C = 2πr   204 cm

2 marks

(b) d = C ÷ π   d = 70 cm

2 marks

Hint
Formulae are given at the front of the paper. Use the π button on your calculator.
π = 3 is only used for estimating.

11 15% of £49.95 = £7.49
The price on the first day of the sale is £49.95 − £7.49 = £42.46
15% of £42.46 = £6.37
The price on the second day of the sale is £42.46 − £6.37 = £36.09
Danny paid £36.09

2 marks

12 (a) $p = 5$, $q = 6$ *3 marks*

(b) Typical working might be:

	x	$10 - x$	area	
	4	6	24	too big
	3	7	21	too big
	2	8	16	much too small
x lies between	2.8	7.2	20.16	a bit too big
2.8 and 2.7 ⟶	2.7	7.3	19.71	a bit too small

3 marks

13 (a) Area = $\dfrac{(a + b)}{2} \times h$ Area = $\dfrac{(50 + 20)}{2} \times 15 = 525\text{m}^2$ *2 marks*

(b) Volume = area of cross section x length = $525 \times 20 = 10\ 500 \text{ m}^3$ *1 mark*

(c) Make a right angled triangle as shown in the diagram.
Then use Pythagoras' theorem to find s.

$s^2 = 30^2 + 15^2$
$s^2 = 900 + 225$
$s^2 = 1125$
$s = \sqrt{1125}$
$s = 33.5$ m   *2 marks*

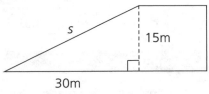

Hint
The formulae are all at the front of Key Stage 3 papers. If you cannot think what to do when finding s, looking at the formulae may jog your memory.

14 (a) Add the number of straws that Pat records as being completely inside a tile to get 93.
300 straws have been dropped altogether so the probability that a straw falls inside a tile is
$\dfrac{93}{300} = 0.31$.

2 marks

(b) If 30 straws are dropped 50 times, that is 1500 straws, we would expect
$1500 \times 0.31 = 465$ straws to be inside. Any number from 450 to 475 would be
reasonable.   *2 marks*

15 (a) $c = 10$ *1 mark*

(b) area = 14.7   *2 marks*

Hint
In part (b) it is better to work out the answer to the part under the square root sign first.

TOTAL

MATHS: ANSWERS

Conversion of score into National Curriculum levels

1 Look at the questions which your child has got right:

Paper 1	questions	1–5	Level 4
	questions	6–10	Level 5
	questions	11–15	Level 6

Paper 2	questions	1–5	Level 5
	questions	6–10	Level 6
	questions	11–15	Level 7

2 Numerical scores can be used to give an approximate National Curriculum level.

Paper 1: maximum marks available 59	
Some work at Level 4 but with many areas to be addressed	less than 15
Working at Level 4 and towards Level 5	16 – 29
Working at Level 5 and towards Level 6	30 – 39
Working at Level 6	40 – 50
Secure at Level 6	51+

Paper 2: maximum marks available 60	
Some work at Level 5 but with many areas to be addressed	less than 15
Working at Level 5 and towards Level 6	16 – 29
Working at Level 6 and towards Level 7	30 – 39
Working at Level 7	40 – 50
Secure at Level 7	51+

Testing your child's science

What do the National Tests cover?

At Key Stage 3 your child will be studying four areas of science in school. These are:

1   Experimental and Investigative Science
2   Life Processes and Living Things
3   Materials and their Properties
4   Physical Processes

The National Tests exclude Experimental and Investigative Science, which usually consists of practical work, and concentrate on science knowledge, which is covered by the other three areas. For the tests in May your child will probably sit two papers; however for ease and simplicity we have provided coverage of the science content in one paper which follows their format.

Tiers of entry

As in previous years, there will be two tiers of tests in science, for pupils working at Levels 3 to 6 and 5 to 7. Pupils considered to be working at Levels 1 and 2 will be assessed through classroom-based tasks, and schools may enter pupils for both the tests and the tasks if they consider this appropriate. There will also be an optional extension paper which will reflect the demand of Level 8 and allow pupils to demonstrate exceptional performance.

Setting the test (time: 60 minutes)

1   Ensure that your child understands where to write the answers in the spaces provided. Explain that some questions will ask for the answer to be drawn rather than written. It is important that answers are drawn as clearly as possible.

2   The test uses some scientific vocabulary (e.g. organ, transparent). If your child has difficulty reading some of these words you may read them out, however you should not explain their meaning. Some answers will require a similar use of a specific scientific word (e.g. condensation) to get a mark. The use of correct scientific language is an important feature from Level 4 on.

3   Allow 60 minutes for the test.

1 Janet was trying to tell her little brother why a motor car is not alive like animals or plants. She wrote out a list of some of the things that they do.

A They take in fuel to give energy.

B They grow.

C They give out waste.

D They can move around.

E They reproduce their own kind.

F They take in air to get oxygen.

G They use light energy to live and grow.

(a) Write out the letter of the one from the list which is **only** true for plants.

_____

(b) Write out the letters of **three** things from the list that cars **and** animals do.

_____

(c) Write out the letter of **two** which are true for animals and plants but **not** motor cars.

_____

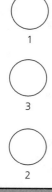

2 The list below contains the names of the main goups of vertebrate animals.

amphibians   reptiles

fish

birds   mammals

(a) Write the correct words from the list to match the descriptions in the table below.

4

Group	Description
	feathery skin, lays shelled eggs on land, breathes air with lungs
	scaly skin, lays shelled eggs on land, breathes air with lungs
	scaly skin, lays eggs in water, breathes through gills
	skin with hair, young develop inside mother and are then fed with milk, breathes air with lungs

(b) Explain what is meant by the word 'vertebrate'

1

_____

_____

TOTAL

3 The diagram below shows some of the main organs in the human body. The dotted line means the organ is behind another one.

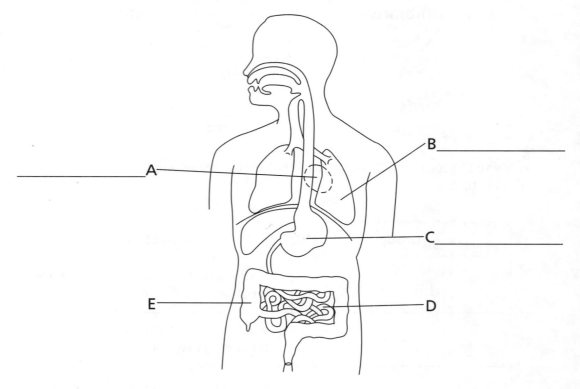

(a) Write the names of organs A, B and C in the spaces next to the letters on the drawing.

(b) Write down the letter of the organ which does the following jobs.

(i) Digestion is completed and food passes into the blood from this organ.

_____

(ii) The body gets rid of carbon dioxide through this organ.

_____

(iii) Water is removed from undigested food from this organ.

_____

(iv) This organ takes in oxygen from the air.

_____

3

1

1

1

1

TOTAL

4 Look at the picture of a motor car then answer the questions about the materials it is made from.

(a) Choose the correct material from the list to show what each part of the car is made of. Write your answers in the **middle** column of the table below.

glass   rubber

plastic

wood   steel

○
4

(b) Choose from the list the property that it is important for each material to have. Write your answers in the right-hand column of the table.

flexible   heavy

strong

transparent   elastic

○
4

part of the car	material	important property
body		
windscreen		
tyres		
seat coverings		

TOTAL

87

5 The diagram below shows the changes of state of water.

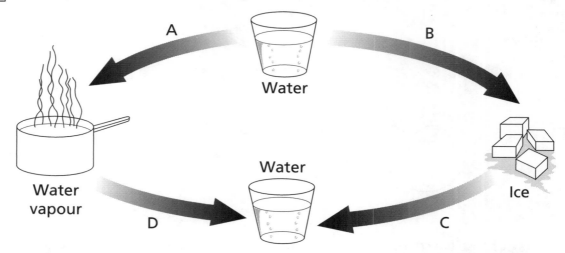

(a) Write down the letters from the diagram against the correct changes below.

melting _____   condensing _____   evaporating _____

(b) Write down the letters from the diagam of the **two** changes where the water loses energy to the surroundings.

_____

(c) In the diagrams below each **o** represents a water molecule.

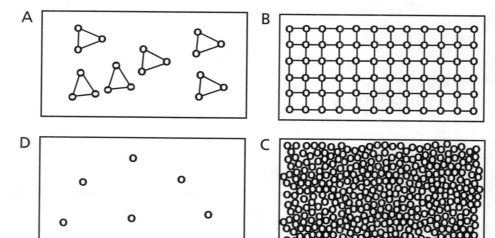

Write down the letters to show which diagram best represents the behaviour of water molecules in:

the ice   _____

the water vapour   _____

3

2

1

1

TOTAL

6 Carlton hung a bar magnet by a thread. Then he put two small boxes containing **either** magnets **or** a piece of iron near to it.

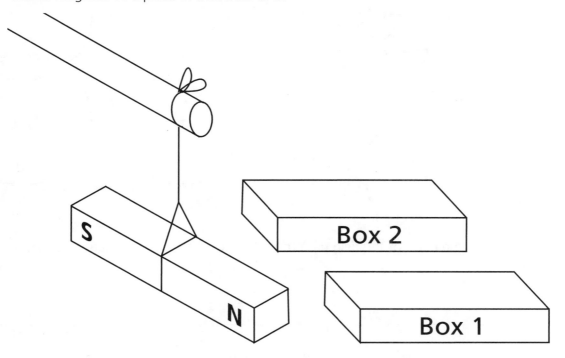

He wrote down what happened each time. His results are in the table.

Pole of magnet	Box 1	Box 2
N	both ends attracted	both ends repelled
S	both ends attracted	both ends attracted

(a) Choose from the drawings below which things might be in Boxes 1 and 2. Write down the letter of the choice in the space

A | S   N | | N   S |

B | N   S | | N   S |

C | |

D | N   S | | S   N |

Box 1 could be _____

Box 2 could be _____

(b) The drawings below show four different magnetic fields made by pairs of magnets.

A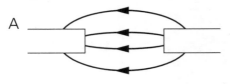

B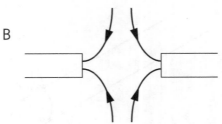

C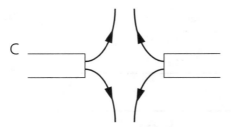

D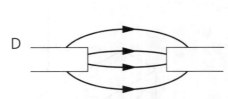

Write the letter of the field pattern that matches the pairs of magnets shown below.

| N | S | _____ |

| S | S | _____ |

| S | N | _____ |

3

TOTAL

4

7 (a) Choose from the list of devices which ones match the energy transfers underneath. Write your answers in the space alongside.

battery　　　**motor car**　　　**waterfall**　　　**light bulb**　　　**microphone**

| electrical | → | light | _____ |

| sound | → | electrical | _____ |

| chemical potential | → | electrical | _____ |

| gravitational potential | → | kinetic | _____ |

(b) In what form is most energy lost in a machine?

1

TOTAL

8 The diagrams below show the stages in the life-cycle of a flowering plant.

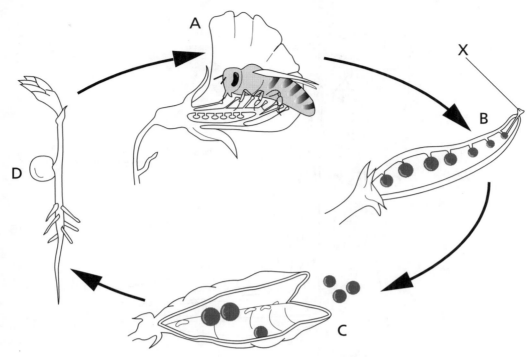

(a) Match the stages from the diagram of the life-cycle against the correct word in the list below. Write down the letters of the stages next to the words.

germination is _____

fertilisation is _____

pollination is _____

1

1

1

(b) What is the stage in the human life cycle that matches stage A? Put a ring around the correct choice from the list below.

birth   sexual intercourse   pregnancy   growth

(c) What is part X called?

_____

1

(d) What is the part of the human reproductive system that matches part X? Put a ring around the correct choice from the list below.

ovary   sperm   testis   ovum

1

TOTAL

9 The diagram below shows some of the bones and muscles of the human shoulder and arm.

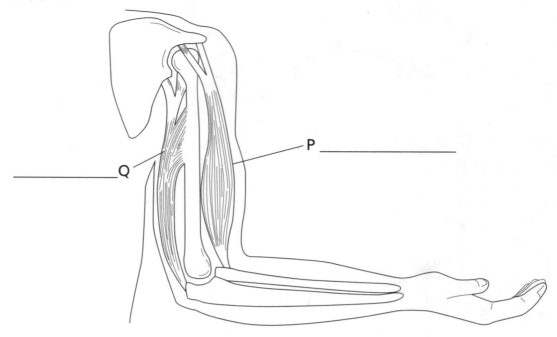

(a) Name the two muscles labelled P and Q. Write the names on the diagram in the spaces next to the letters.

(b) Explain the roles of the two muscles in bending and straightening the arm at the elbow.

_____

_____

_____

_____

(c) Explain why muscles need to work in pairs like this.

_____

_____

(d) Which word from the list below is used to describe pairs of muscle like P and Q. Put a ring around the correct answer.

antagonistic   **alternate**   **opposite**   **synergistic**

TOTAL

10 The table below gives some information about five elements A–E. Read it carefully and then answer the questions below.

Element	Appearance at room temperature	Melting point (°C)	Boiling point (°C)	Thermal conductivity	Electrical conductivity
A	shiny silvery	−39	357	good	good
B	colourless	−214	−196	very poor	very poor
C	shiny red	1083	2582	excellent	excellent
D	shiny grey	1539	2887	good	good
E	dull yellow	119	445	poor	poor

(a) Write down the letters of the **two** elements that are non-metals.

_____

(b) Write down the letter of the element that is a gas at room temperature.

_____

(c) Write down the letter of the element that is most likely to be brittle at room temperature.

_____

(d) Write down the letter of the element that is best suited for each of the following jobs.

(i) tripods for use with the bunsen burner   _____

(ii) the liquid in the laboratory thermometer   _____

(iii) wiring for a house   _____

2

1

1

3

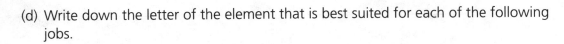

93

(e) Give **two** reasons for your choice of answer for part (ii).

_____

_____

2

(f) State **one** other property that the material used for wiring must have that is **not** shown in the table.

_____

1

TOTAL

11 The diagram shows a section through a rock formation in a place where the days are often very hot but the nights can be very cold.

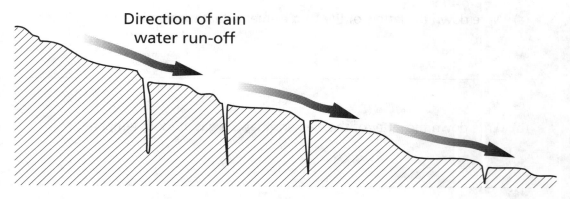

Direction of rain water run-off

(a) Explain how these conditions would cause weathering of the rocks in **two** ways.

way 1 _____

_____

way 2 _____

_____

2

(b) State two other causes of weathering.

_____

_____

2

TOTAL

12 The drawing shows four forces acting on an aeroplane.

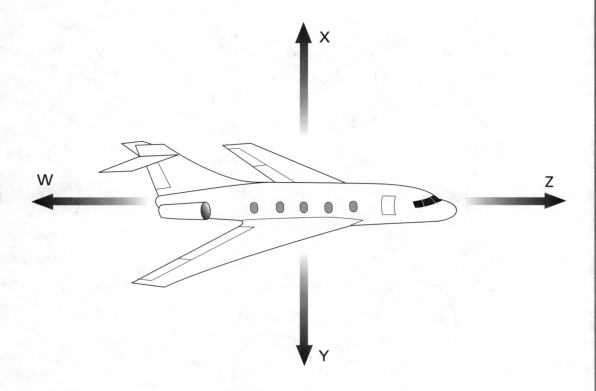

(a) Which one is gravity?

_____

1

(b) Which one has to get bigger to make the aeroplane go faster?

_____

1

(c) Which one is caused by friction with the air?

_____

1

(d) The plane is flying level with the ground. The weight of the plane is 100 000 N. What can you tell about force X?

_____

1

(e) This type of plane **cannot** fly straight upwards like fighter planes can. What does this tell you about the biggest value that force Z can have?

_____

1

TOTAL

13 The diagram shows the Earth's position at different stages in its path around the Sun.

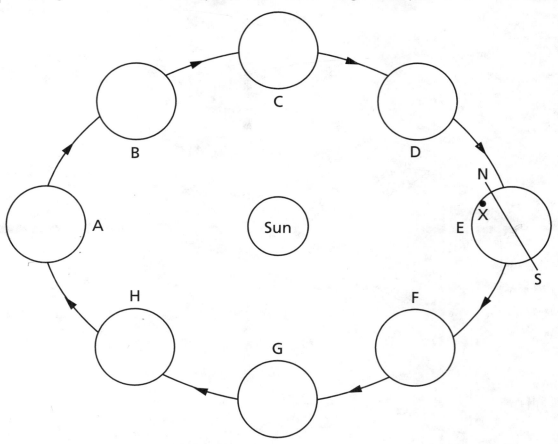

(a) The point marked X represents Great Britain. Tick the correct choice below to show what time of day and year it is.

midday on midsummer's day _____

midnight on midsummer's day _____

midday on midwinter's day _____

midnight on midwinter's day _____

(b) Draw the positions of the North and South Poles and the Equator when the Earth is in position A.

(c) Write down the letters of the **two** positions of the Earth when the length of the day and night in Great Britain will be equal.

_____

(d) What season is represented by the section between B and D?

_____

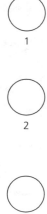

1

2

1

1

TOTAL

14 (a) Look carefully at the circuit diagram below then fill in the table to show how many bulbs will be lit for each set of switches closed.

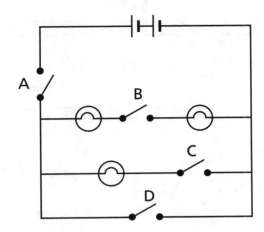

Switches closed	Number of bulbs lit
A and B	
A, B and C	
A, B, C and D	

3

(b) In the circuit below all the bulbs and ammeters are exactly the same.

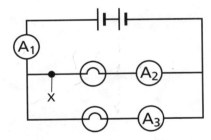

(i) What is being measured in this circuit?

_____

1

(ii) The reading on A_3 is 0.4 amps. What are the readings on A_1 and A_2?

A_1 _____

1

A_2 _____

1

(iii) If another bulb was placed at point X in the circuit what would A_2 now read?

_____

1

1

TOTAL

1 The table below shows the percentages of food classes (P, Q, R, S) in a number of food items.

Food item	Food classes			
	P	Q	R	S
salmon	6.0	0.0	20.0	74.0
carrot	0.0	5.0	1.0	94.0
butter	81.0	1.0	0.0	18.0
fried potato	9.0	37.0	4.0	50.0
raw egg	12.0	0.0	12.0	76.0
cornflakes	0.5	88.0	8.0	3.5

(a) Write down which of the food classes from the list below matches the letters P, Q, R and S.

proteins   water

vitamins

carbohydrates   fats

P is   _____

Q is   _____

R is   _____

S is   _____

(b) Give the **main** use in the human body for each of the food classes below.

protein

_____

carbohydrate

_____

2 A gardener took a number of cuttings from the plant shown in the drawing and planted each one in a pot of compost. He sold the cuttings to different people.

(a) What does the gardener know must be true about the genetic material in the cuttings he has taken?

_____

1

(b) When the cuttings were fully grown they were of different sizes and shapes. Write down **three** possible reasons for these differences.

_____

_____

_____

3

(c) The flowers on the plant are large and a deep red colour. The ancestors of the plant that grew in the wild had flowers that were smaller and a much lighter red. Explain how the modern deep red variety could have been produced from the wild plant.

_____

_____

_____

_____

2

TOTAL

3 Here is a food web showing some of the feeding relationships between the living things in a pond.

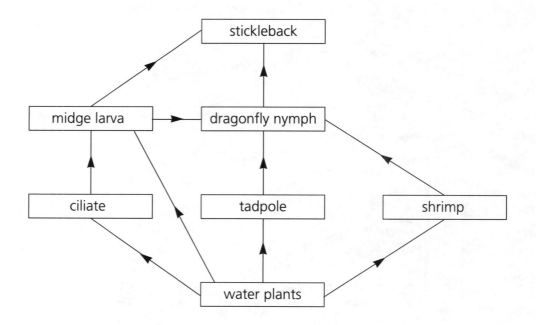

(a) Which organism in this food web is the producer?

1

_____

(b) Which organisms are **primary** consumers **only**?

1

_____

(c) Which organism is **both** a primary and a secondary consumer?

1

_____

(d) What might be the effect on the tadpole population if the shrimp population was removed? Explain your answer fully.

_____

_____

1

_____

(e) Complete the word equation below to show the process of photosynthesis going on in the water plants.

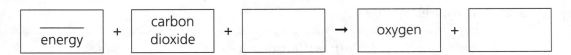

| _____ energy | + | carbon dioxide | + | | → | oxygen | + | |

○ 2

(f) Use the equation to explain how the water plants can benefit the populations of water animals **apart** from providing them with food.   2 marks

_____

_____

(g) Use the equation to explain how the animal populations could help to increase the rate of photosynthesis.

_____

_____

○ 2

(h) There are two types of water plants in the pond.

- one-celled algae

- large water weeds (up to 1 m long)

Which of the following pyramids of numbers represents the food chain:

large water → tadpole → dragonfly → stickleback
weeds   nymph

Put a ring around the correct choice.

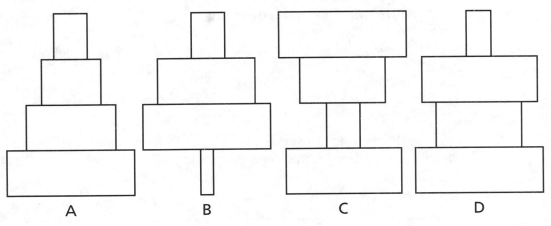

A   B   C   D

○ 1

TOTAL

4 A laboratory technician forgot to put the lables on some bottles containing solutions for an experiment on acids and alkalis.

To find out what was in the bottles he used Universal Indicator and a pH scale to test the solutions. Here are the results.

Solution	Colour with Indicator	Label
A	dark purple	
B	yellow–orange	
C	green	

(a) Use words from the list below to label the solutions. Write your answers in the table.

strong   neutral

alkali

acid   weak

(b) A wasp sting is alkaline. What would be the best pH of solution to put on it? Put a ring around your choice.

pH 1   pH 5   pH 7   pH 12

(c) Give **two** reasons for choice for part (b).

_____

_____

(d) Acid rain contains sulphuric acid that can poison lakes and kill the fish in them. People sometimes try to prevent this by putting lumps of limestone (calcium carbonate) around the edges of the lake. The acid water running into the lake reacts with the limestone and gas is given off.

(i) Fill in the boxes below to complete the word equation for the reaction.

calcium carbonate	+		→		+		+	water

(ii) What would you expect to **see** as the acid rainwater reacted with the limestone (apart from the limestone disappearing)?

_____

(iii) What kind of chemical reaction is taking place? Put a ring around the answer from the list below.   1 mark

oxidation   neutralisation

combustion   thermal decomposition

1

TOTAL

5 The diagram shows a section cut through the upper layers of the Earth's crust.

Earth's surface

B   E   Limestone

Limestone

C   F   Shale

Magma
intrusion
A

D   Limestone   G

(a) Which letter shows an igneous rock?

_____

1

(b) Which letter shows the **youngest** sedimentary rock?

_____

1

(c) Which letter **or letters** shows metamorphic rock?

_____

1

(d) What is the name of rock formed in regions B and D?

_____

1

(e) Describe how you would expect the rock formed at B to be different in structure from the rock formed at D.

_____

_____

1

(f) Give reasons for your answer to part (e).

_____

_____

6 A pupil dropped a sample of a metallic element into a test-tube containing a solution of a salt of another metal. She noted whether there was a reaction or not.

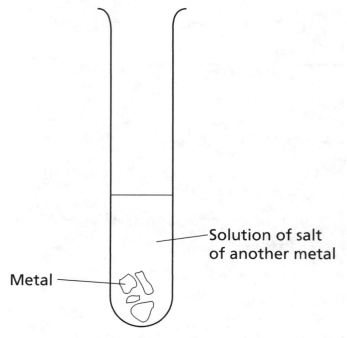

Metal

Solution of salt of another metal

She repeated the experiment with 4 metallic elements and their compounds. The results are shown in the table. A tick means a reaction took place.

metallic element	compound			
	salt of element A	salt of element B	salt of element C	salt of element D
A	not done	X	✓	X
B	✓	not done	✓	✓
C	X	X	not done	X
D	✓	X	✓	not done

(a) Write out the letters of the metals in order of reactivity starting with the highest.

_____

(b) The four metals are:

iron   magnesium   copper   aluminium

Enter them into the reactivity table below.

lithium

_____

_____

_____

_____

silver

(c) Use the table to explain why silver is used as a jewellery metal.

_____

_____

○ 1

(d) A silver compound often used in the laboratory has the formula $Ag\,NO_3$.
What is the name of the compound?

_____

○ 1

(e) Write out the elements in this compound.

_____

○ 1

(f) Name the two products that would be formed by the reaction between this compound and iron.

_____

○ 1

(g) The products can easily be separated from each other by filtration. Explain why the elements in $Ag\,NO_3$ cannot be separated from each other by this kind of method.

_____

_____

○ 1

TOTAL

7 (a) Diagram A on the left below shows two light rays coming from the edge of a coin in an empty china mug. The rays miss the eye of the observer. Diagram B on the right shows the same mug now filled with water.

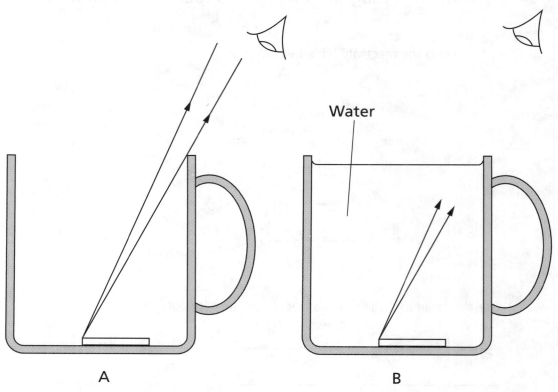

Water

A   B

(i) Draw the path of the rays on diagram B to show how the eye can now see the edge of the coin.

(ii) Show where the eye will now see the image of the coin.

(b) What is the name given to the bending of light in this way?

_____

(c) The mug has blue and white stripes on the outside. It is left in a room with a red light on the ceiling.

(i) What colour will the white stripes appear in the red light? Explain why this is so.

_____

_____

(ii) What colour will the blue stripes appear in the red light? Explain why this is so.

_____

_____

1

1

1

2

2

TOTAL

8 The table below shows some information about the first 5 planets from the Sun.

Planet	Diameter (km)	Average distance from the Sun (million km)	Time to orbit Sun (Earth days)	Time to rotate on axis
X	5000	58	88	88 Earth days
Venus	12 200	108	225	242 Earth days
Earth	13 000	151	365	24 hours
Mars	6 800	229	690	24 hours
Jupiter	143 000	778	4 400	10 hours

(a) What is the name of planet X?

_____

(b) Which planet has a longer day than its year?

_____

(c) On which planet or planets would you expect an astronaut to weigh more than on the surface of the Earth?

_____

(d) Give a reason for your answer.

_____

_____

(e) What keeps the planets in their orbit?

_____

(f) What is approximately the closest that Jupiter could get to Mars? Show your working.

_____

_____

(g) What is approximately the furthest that Earth could get from Venus? Show your working.

_____

_____

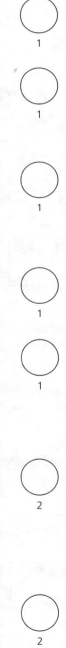

1

1

1

1

1

2

2

(h) From the Earth, Venus is the brightest object in the night sky apart from the Moon. Give two reasons why it appears brighter than Jupiter even though Jupiter is much larger.

_____

_____

9 The diagram below shows an electric bell which gives a continuous ringing (or buzzing) sound.
Explain step by step how the continuous ringing is produced.

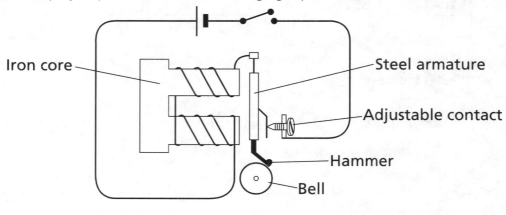

_____

_____

_____

_____

10 A fisherman sits on a three-legged stool on ice on a lake. The fisherman weighs 780 N. The stool weighs 30 N. The legs of the stool each have a cross-sectional area of 6 cm$_2$.

(a) What is the total force that the fisherman puts on the ice as he sits on the stool?

_____ N

(b) What pressure does he put on the ice when both feet are off the ground? Give your answer in the correct units.

_____

_____

_____

SCIENCE
Answers

Paper 1

Levels 3-6

Question	Answers	Marks

1 (a) G — *1 mark*
(b) **Any three of:** A, C, D, F — *3 marks*
(c) B and E — *2 marks*
Total 6 marks

2 (a) **In order:** birds, reptiles, fish, mammals — *4 marks*
(b) Animal with backbone/internal skeleton made of bone — *1 mark*
Total 5 marks

3 (a) A = heart, B = lung, C = stomach — *3 marks*
(b) (i) D, (ii) B, (iii) E, (iv) B — *4 marks*
Total 7 marks

4 (a) **In order down table:** steel, glass, rubber, plastic — *4 marks*
(b) **In order down table:** strong, transparent, elastic, flexible — *4 marks*
Total 8 marks

5 (a) **melting:** C   **condensing:** D   **evaporating:** A — *3 marks*
(b) B and D — *2 marks*
(c) **ice:** B   **water vapour:** D — *2 marks*
Total 7 marks

6 (a) **Box 1:** C   **Box 2:** D — *2 marks*
(b) **In order from top:** D, B, A — *3 marks*
Total 5 marks

7 (a) **In order:** light bulb, microphone, battery, waterfall — *4 marks*
(b) heat — *1 mark*
Total 5 marks

8 (a) **germination:** D   **fertilisation:** B   **pollination:** A — *3 marks*
(b) sexual intercourse — *1 mark*
(c) pollen grain — *1 mark*
(d) sperm — *1 mark*
Total 6 marks

9 (a) P is biceps   Q is triceps — *2 marks*
(b) **idea 1** biceps contracts (or shortens) to raise forearm (or flex/ bend arm at elbow)
idea 2 triceps relaxes at this time
idea 3 triceps contracts (or shortens) to lower forearm (or extend/ straighten arm) at elbow
idea 4 biceps relaxes at this time
NB The important idea is that one pulls while other relaxes and vice versa.
Also if muscles are named wrongly in part   (a) mark according to the letters
so muscle P **must** flex the arm   (b) any **three** ideas in either order — *3 marks*
(c) **idea 1** muscles are soft
idea 2 muscles can only pull not push — *2 marks*
(d) antagonistic — *1 mark*
Total 8 marks

10 (a) B and E — *2 marks*
(b) B — *1 mark*
(c) E — *1 mark*
(d) (i) D   (ii) A   (iii) C — *3 marks*
(e) liquid at room temperature — *1 mark*
good conductor of heat — *1 mark*
(f) flexible/ductile — *1 mark*
Total 10 marks

11 (a) rocks expand and contract and bits break off *1 mark*
water in cracks freezes and expands so bits break off *1 mark*
(b) **Any two of:** 1 growth of plant roots/2 wetting and drying/3 reaction by
acid rain (or oxidation)/4 erosion due to wind **or** water **or** rain *2 marks*
Total 4 marks

12 (a) Y *1 mark*
(b) Z *1 mark*
(c) W *1 mark*
(d) It is 100 000 N/it is the same *1 mark*
(e) It cannot be larger than 100 000 N/plane's weight. **or** It must be equal to or
less than 100 000 N/plane's weight *1 mark*
Total 5 marks

13 (a) midday in midsummer *1 mark*
(b)

1 mark for poles
1 mark for equator

(c) C and G (**both** needed for one mark) *1 mark*
(d) spring *1 mark*
Total 5 marks

14 (a) **A and B:** 2   **A, B and C:** 3   **A, B, C and D:** 0 *3 marks*
(b) (i) current/flow of charge *1 mark*
(ii) A_1 0.8 amps A_2 0.4 amps *2 marks*
(iii) A_2 would read 0.2 amps *1 mark*
Total 7 marks

Total marks for Paper 1 = 88

Paper 2
Levels 5-7

Question	Answers	Marks

1 (a) P = fat,   Q = carbohydrate,   R = protein,   S = water *4 marks*
(b) **proteins:** growth/repair,   **carbohydrates:** energy *2 marks*
Total 6 marks

2 (a) It is the same in all of them *1 mark*
(b) **any three of:** different amounts of light
different amounts of water
different amounts of minerals/ nutrients
kept at different temperatures *3 marks*
(c) **Idea 1:** Select plants with largest and reddest flowers and breed these together.
Idea 2: Offspring will have some larger and redder than before.
Idea 3: Repeat process over many generations. *3 marks*
Total 7 marks

3 (a) water plants *1 mark*
(b) ciliates, tadpoles, shrimps   **all** for one mark *1 mark*
(c) midge larva *1 mark*
(d) **either:** increases because has more plants to eat
or decreases because the dragonfly nymph preys on it more *1 mark*
(e) **left side**   light energy   water
right side   carbohydrate/sugar/starch/glucose *2 marks*
(f) **Idea 1:** The plants produce oxygen as a waste product.
Idea 2: The animals use this for respiration/breathe it in. *2 marks*

(g)   **Idea 1:** The animals use this for respiration/breathe it in. The animals produce/breathe out carbon dioxide (in respiration)
Idea 2: The animals use this for respiration/breathe it in. This is used as raw material for photosynthesis.   *2 marks*

(h)   B   *1 mark*

Total 11 marks

4   (a)   A = strong alkali,   B = weak acid,   C = neutral   *3 marks*

(b)   pH 5   *1 mark*

(c)   acid to neutralise/cancel out the alkali   *1 mark*
weak acid is not dangerous/strong acid would be   *1 mark*

(d)   (i)   **left side**   sulphuric acid   *1 mark*
right side   calcium sulphate + carbon dioxide   *1 mark*
(ii)   bubbles/fizzing/effervescence   *1 mark*

(e)   neutralisation   *1 mark*

Total 10 marks

5   (a)   A   *1 mark*

(b)   E   *1 mark*

(c)   B, C, D   **all** needed for one mark   *1 mark*

(d)   marble   *1 mark*

(e)   Rock B would be more granular/less crystalline **or** Rock D would be more crystalline **or** Rock B less completely metamorphosed/transformed from sedimentary structure   *1 mark*

(f)   Idea of less heat and pressure at rock B to cause metamorphosis   *1 mark*

Total 6 marks

6   (a)   **In order:** B, D, A, C   **All** correct for 2 marks
Must have B first and C last for 1 mark   *2 marks*

(b)   **In order from top:** magnesium, aluminium, iron, copper   *1 mark*

(c)   **Idea 1:** Silver is bottom of table so very unreactive.
Idea 2: So does not react with air/oxygen/water so stays shiny   *2 marks*

(d)   silver nitrate   *1 mark*

(e)   silver, nitrogen, oxygen   **all** correct for 1 mark   *1 mark*

(f)   **In either order:** iron nitrate + silver   both for 1 mark   *1 mark*

(g)   **Idea that:** in the compound the elements/particles are bonded/chemically joined together   *1 mark*

Total 9 marks

7   (a)   (i) and (ii)

(i)   lines must continue to diverge
(ii)   image must be at meeting point of lines   *2 marks*

(b)   refraction   *1 mark*

(c)   (i)   red   *1 mark*
idea of: the red light is reflected from the white: *1 mark*
(ii)   black   *1 mark*
idea of: the red light is absorbed by the blue so nothing is reflected: *1 mark*

Total 7 marks

8   (a)   Mercury   *1 mark*

(b)   Venus   *1 mark*

(c)   Jupiter   *1 mark*

(d)   **Idea that:** planet is larger so gravity is stronger   *1 mark*

(e)   gravity   *1 mark*

(f)   778 million - 229 million
= 548 million km
(allow rounding off to 550 million km)   *2 marks*

(g)   151+108 million km
= 259 million km
(allow rounding off to 260 million km)   *2 marks*

(h) closer to the Sun so reflects more light
closer to Earth
Accept idea that: Venus is more reflective

2 marks
Total 11 marks

9 Any 4 of:
Switch is closed and current flows so iron core becomes a magnet/electromagnet.
Magnet attracts the armature which strikes bell.
Armature breaks the contact as it moves.
This switches off current so core not magnetic.
Armature springs back and remakes contact so process starts again.

Total 4 marks

10 (a) 810
45
N/cm^2

1 mark
1 mark
1 mark
Total 3 marks

Total marks for Paper 1 = 74

SCIENCE

Conversion of score into National Curriculum levels

Paper 1: maximum marks available 88

Working at Level 2	less than 21
Working at Level 3	22 – 34
Working at Level 4	35 – 48
Working at Level 5	49 – 61
Working at Level 6	61+

Paper 2: maximum marks available 74

Working at Level 3	less than 15
Working at Level 4	15 – 21
Working at Level 5	22 – 37
Working at Level 6	38 – 49
Working at Level 7	50+